DEDICATION

to those men and women
who have given so much of their talent
that man may walk among the stars

Nick Oddo
Peter M. Topaz
Publishers

LeRoi Smith
Editor

William Reid
Art Director

Peter S. Chaffey—Assistant Art Director

Cover Art: Don Irwin

Title Page Art: Robert Schaar

Graphic Artists: Rod Van Uchelen, Ronald Chaffey

The typeface **Galaxia**, used on front cover and various editorial headlines was designed especially for this book by William Reid.

Contributing Editors
James Aswell, Frederick C. Durant III, Don Dwiggins, Dr. Ellis B. Miner Peter Abbott

Administration
Barbara A. Jones
Patricia E. Lane
Gretchen Stadler

Editorial & Composition
Shirley Bolton—Production Director
Helen Epperson, Doris Parker
Roberta Tumbiolo, Betty Wells

Research
Al Davidson
Patricia Walsh

Published by Classic Press Inc., San Rafael, California, with Professional Press, Inc., Chicago, Illinois. © 1969 by Classic Press Inc. and Professional Press, Inc. First printing, September, 1969. Printed in the U.S.A.

Photographs and illustrations used in this publication courtesy of Smithsonian Institution, North American-Rockwell, the California Institute of Technology, and the Carnegie Institution of Washington.

WHY EXPLORE THE MOON?

Let us look first at why lunar exploration is of great importance to our nation. To the scientific world, there is great interest in the origin and history of the Moon and its relation to the Earth, and to the solar system. Was it formed with the Earth, or captured later? Are there clues to the origin of life? To quote the President's Science Advisory Committee, "Answers to these questions may profoundly affect our views of the evolution of the solar system and its place, as well as man's, in the larger scheme of things."

Many planets have Moons, but ours is the largest in relation to its planet. This implies that the two bodies may have been formed in the same manner at the same time. If true, the Moon may be a book containing the secret of the Earth's first billion years of life. This record is lost on the earth which is subjected to the wear and tear of erosion by atmosphere and water.

Until now natural phenomena that can affect man could be studied only on Earth. Now we believe many things that happen on Earth also happen on the Moon. By comparing similarities and contrasting differences, man may be able to arrive at a greater understanding of the fundamental processes that affect the Earth; for example, the mechanisms that cause earthquakes and volcanic eruptions, and the processes responsible for concentrating ore deposits. The orbits of Apollo 8 and the Lunar Orbiters were disturbed by mass concentrations beneath the circular lunar seas. These may be huge meteors that struck the Moon with such force that they melted and sank into the interior, or they may be iron deposits.

Another objective of lunar exploration is to learn about man as a space explorer — his capabilities and limitations. Some day man will move on to other planets; the Moon is a training ground.

It is difficult to look far ahead. We don't have the basic information which early lunar landings will furnish and we can only speculate today about the feasibility of the Moon as a base for an observatory or a permanent science station — about exploiting its environment of low gravity and high vacuum — about its potential for natural resources.

The eventual goal of a lunar base would bring into focus the steps that must precede it, just as Apollo was important in establishing the objectives of Mercury, Gemini, Surveyor, and Orbiter. Critical to future considerations of a lunar base goal is information on the lunar environment, location of natural resources and strategic sites that could serve multiple purposes. A long-range goal like the lunar base would direct technological advances, stimulate public interest, and attain subsidiary objectives with Earth application such as food synthesis, environmental control, and recovery of useful elements from rock.

Dr. Goerge E. Mueller
NASA Associate Administrator For
Manned Space Flight
Excerpt from statement to Congress
March 11, 1969

A few cautious steps into outer space and mankind is launched on his greatest adventure. An awesome ocean to cross in an effort to find out more about himself; a prairie hostile and uncaring for him or his kind. Still, man will press his search for knowledge, making an adjustment where necessary in order to survive, and eventually, to conquer. The space pioneer is driven by the same irresistible urge that sent Columbus across uncharted seas and frontiersmen to distant mountain peaks, an unrelenting desire to know what lies beyond. Science has a good idea of what is "out there," but the final proof is left to the astronaut. Hurtling along at thousands of miles an hour, the spaceman lives in a lonely and forboding vacuum, at once frightening and yet beautiful beyond earthbound understanding.

THE NOW OF SPACE

LIFTOFF!

Nimbus Ten

Gemini VII

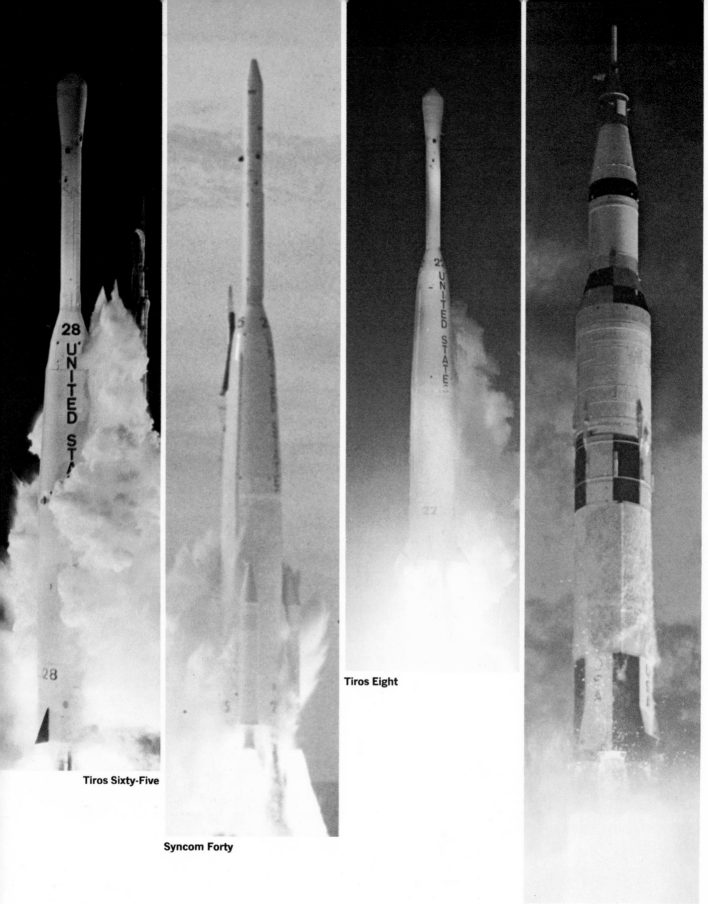

Tiros Sixty-Five

Syncom Forty

Tiros Eight

Saturn V

Schweickart's Apollo 9 spacewalk.

ABOARD
THE
SPACE
CAPSULE

Scott in hatch of Apollo 9 CM.

The spacecraft cockpit is tight quarters.

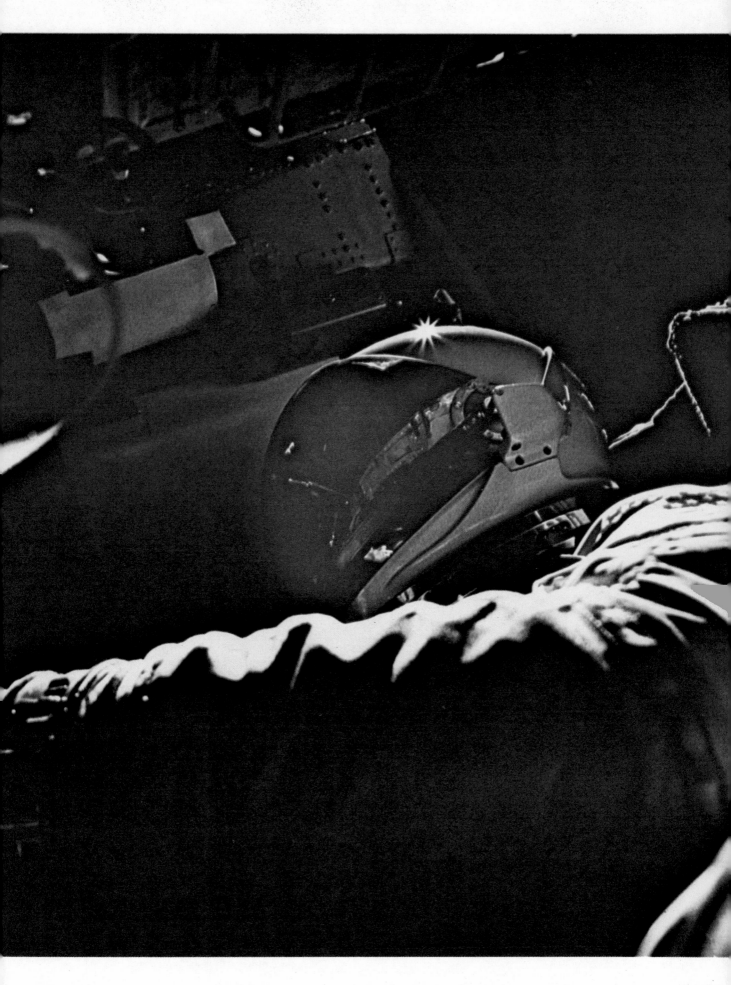

THE VIEW FROM SPACE

Left — Our planet earth is
a beautiful sight to astronauts,
with blue and white surface
of ocean and clouds. It seems
to be lonely and far away.

View of the moon from Apollo 8.

Lunar surface is marked by craters.

Looking south over Baja California.

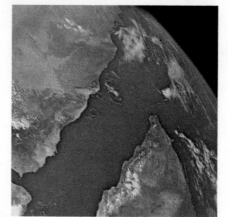

Water between Ethiopia and Arabia.

MAN IN SPACE

Edward H. White takes a spectacular walk
in space from Gemini 4 flight. Umbilical cord
connects to spacecraft.

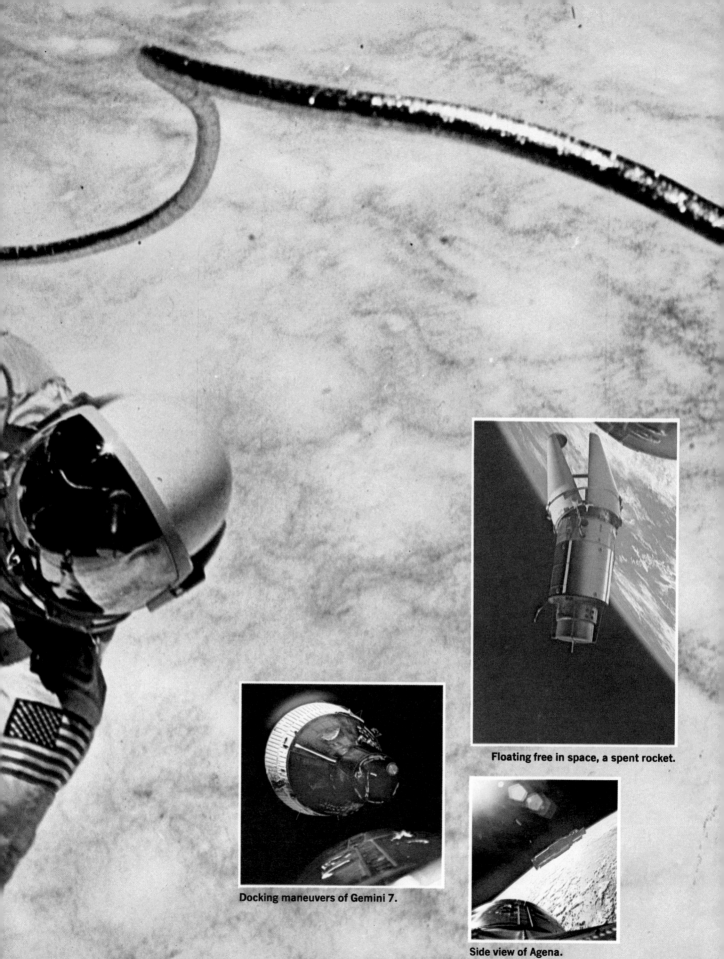

Floating free in space, a spent rocket.

Docking maneuvers of Gemini 7.

Side view of Agena.

SPACE HARDWARE

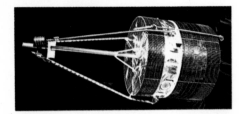

Pioneer 8.

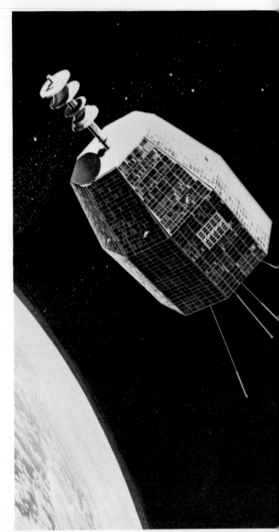

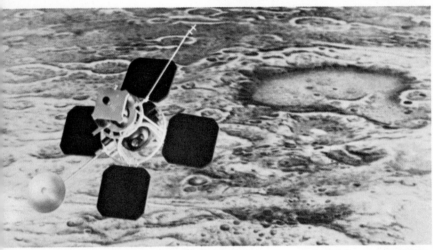

Lunar Orbiter.   **Relay-23.**

Tiros 7.

Right — Syncom II-22.

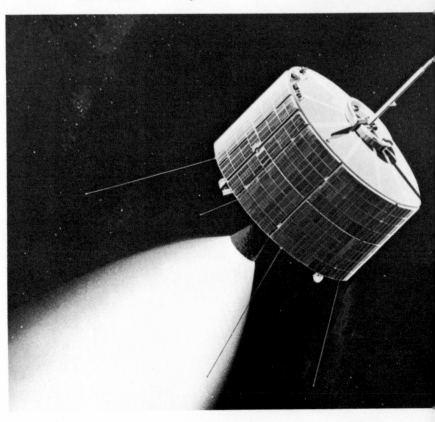

Mariner E for Venus mission.

Application Technology Satellite.

Lunar Module.

Telstar.

MOONSHIP ONE

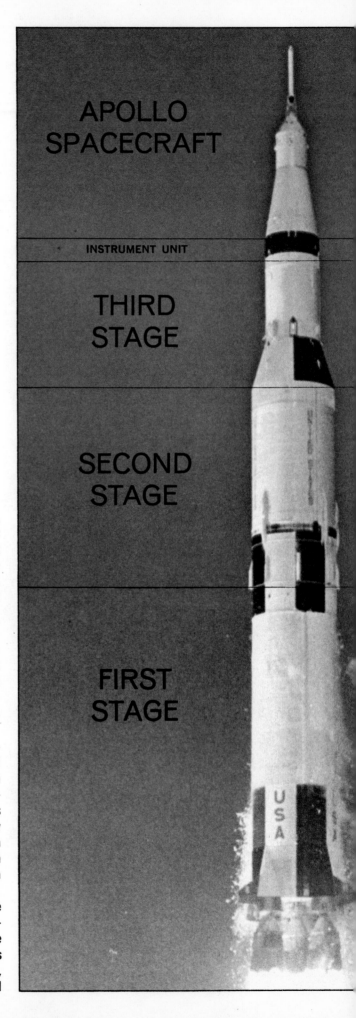

APOLLO SPACECRAFT

INSTRUMENT UNIT

THIRD STAGE

SECOND STAGE

FIRST STAGE

BY DON DWIGGINS

It stands on Launch Complex 39 at Cape Kennedy, six stories taller than the Statue of Liberty on her pedestal, weighing 13 times as much. They call it Apollo, this marvel of technological perfection poised atop a monster Saturn V launch vehicle, dazzling as the namesake, the Greek god of light and twin brother of Artemis, goddess of the moon.

The Apollo spacecraft itself, apart from the Saturn V rocket booster, consists of half a dozen intricately-wedded components towering 363 feet 4 inches, wrought by the world's best engineering brains and skilled craftsmen from a single dream—to put a man on the moon and bring him back during the decade of the 1960's.

Strangely enough, Apollo was already an advanced lunar exploration program more than a full year before the late President John F. Kennedy, on May 25, 1961, committed this nation to the national goal of lunar conquest. Said Kennedy: "Now is the time to take longer strides, time for a great new American enterprise, time for this nation to take a clearly leading role in space achievement, which in many ways may hold the key to our future on earth."

It was President Kennedy's foresight that put the Apollo Project on the road as the greatest engineering effort of all time, one that would involve hundreds of thousands of people and many billions of dollars. And like the tragic death of the President, Project Apollo too would endure disaster and trial

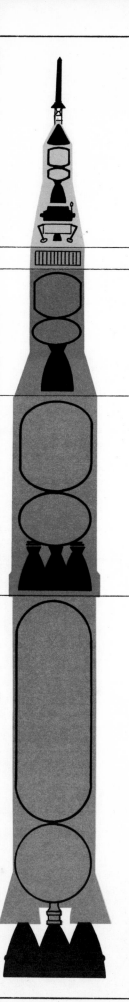

The Command Module is the control center for the spacecraft; it provides living and working quarters for the three-man crew for the entire flight, except for the period when two men will be in the LM for the descent to the moon and return.

The Service Module houses the electrical power subsystem, reaction control engines, part of the environmental control subsystem, and the service propulsion subsystem including the main propulsion engine for insertion into orbit around the moon, and for return from the moon.

The Lunar Module will carry two men from the orbiting CSM down to the surface of the moon, provide a base of operations on the moon, and return the two men to a rendezvous with the CSM in orbit.

Command
Module . . . . 13 feet in diameter; weight, 11,000 pounds.
Service Module . 13 feet in diameter, 22 feet in height; weight, 52,000 pounds; 22,000-pound thrust engine.
Lunar Module . . Two stages; total weight, 32,000 pounds. Descent engine's thrust can be varied from 1,050 to 10,500 pounds.

This unit contains guidance and control equipment for the launch vehicle.

Diameter . . . . . 21.7 feet, Height — 58.3 ft.
Weight . . . . 258,038 lbs. fueled
25,300 lbs. dry
Engines . . . . . . One J-2
Propellants . . . Liquid oxygen (19,600 gals.)
Liquid hydrogen (77,675 gals.)
Thrust . . . . 232,000 lbs. (first burn)
211,000 lbs. (second burn)

The third stage has two important operations during the Project Apollo lunar mission. After the second stage drops away, the third ignites and burns for about two minutes to place itself and the spacecraft into the desired earth orbit. At the proper time during this earth parking orbit, the third stage is re-ignited to speed the Apollo spacecraft to escape velocity of 24,900 miles per hour.

Diameter . . . . . 33 feet, Height — 81.5 feet
Weight . . . . 1,069,033 lbs. fueled
84,600 lbs. dry
Engines . . . . . . Five J-2
Propellants . . . Liquid oxygen (86,700 gals.)
Liquid hydrogen (281,550 gals.)
Thrust . . . . 1,150,000 lbs.
Interstage . . . . . 10,305 lbs.

The second stage burns over one ton of propellants per second during about six and one-half minutes of operation to take the vehicle to an altitude of about 108 miles and a speed of near orbital velocity, which in this case is about 17,400 miles-per-hour. It is 33 feet in diameter and 81½ feet long.

Diameter . . . . . 33 feet, Height — 138 feet
Weight . . . . 5,026,200 lbs. fueled
295,600 lbs. dry
Engines . . . . . . Five F-1
Propellants . . . . Liquid oxygen (347,300 gals.)
RP-1 (Kerosene) — (211,140 gals.)
Thrust . . . . 7,700,000 lbs.

The first stage burns over 15 tons of propellants per second during its two and one-half minutes of operation to take the vehicle to a height of about 36 miles and to a speed of about 6,000 miles-per-hour. The stage is 138 feet long and 33 feet in diameter.

SATURN V — MIGHTIEST SPACE VEHICLE

The Saturn V, 363 feet tall with the Apollo spacecraft in place, generates enough thrust to place a 125-ton payload into a 105 nm circular Earth orbit or boost a smaller payload to the vicinity of any planet in the solar system. It can boost about 50 tons to lunar orbit. The thrust of the three propulsive stages range from more than 7.7 million pounds for the booster to 230,000 pounds for the third stage at operating altitude. Including the instrument unit, the launch vehicle is 281 feet tall.

THRUST

Rocket propulsion is a practical application of Newton's Third Law (where there is action, there must be a reaction of equal magnitude in the opposite direction). It involves forces and motion caused by rearward ejection of matter from the propelled body. In the case of a rocket this means the creation of a forward thrust by the rearward ejection of high-velocity combustion gases.

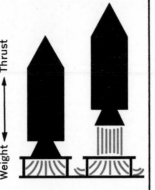

FUNCTION

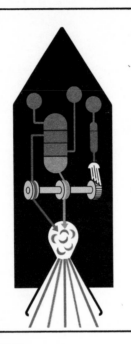

- FUEL
- OXIDIZER
- COMPRESSED GAS
- STEAM OR VAPOR

Pump-fed version (as are F-1 and J-2 engines). This system is entirely self-contained and can operate in the vacuum of space. For optimum performance, this system has to be carefully adjusted and trimmed by ground firings to allow simultaneous depletion of both propellants.

COMBUSTION PROCESS

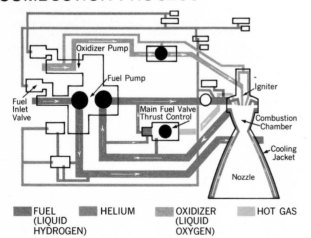

Oxidizer Pump
Fuel Pump
Igniter
Fuel Inlet Valve
Main Fuel Valve Thrust Control
Combustion Chamber
Cooling Jacket
Nozzle

- FUEL (LIQUID HYDROGEN)
- HELIUM
- OXIDIZER (LIQUID OXYGEN)
- HOT GAS

Hydrogen, liquid at 423° F. below zero, enters at fuel inlet valve, passes through the fuel pump and moves through the cooling jacket around the exhaust nozzle of the combustion chamber, cooling the walls and protecting them from destructive heat of the burning mixture inside. As the hydrogen moves through this cooling jacket it becomes a gas. This gas, still cold at −100°, expands through a turbine to furnish the mechanical power needed to pump more hydrogen into the combustion chamber. The pump sequence is controlled by helium which actuates switches. The same turbine also furnishes power to keep liquid oxygen flowing through pumps toward the combustion chamber.

ENGINES FOR MANNED FLIGHT

F-1

First Stage.
Burns Liquid Oxygen and Kerosine.
Develops 1,500,000 Pounds of Thrust.
Weight, 10 Tons.
Height 18 Feet.
Nozzle Exit
Diameter 14 Feet.

J-2

Second Stage.
Burns Liquid Oxygen and Liquid Hydrogen.
Develops 200,000 Pounds of Thrust.
Designed to Operate in the Vacuum of Space.

Saturn V first stage.

by fire, before soaring off to conquer other worlds.

First announced as a NASA program at an industry conference on July 29, 1960, Project Apollo presented a major challenge without precedent—no one had ever designed a moonship before. No one, that is, unless you consider the fictional concepts of science writers like Jules Verne and H. G. Wells, who believed the best way to get there was to shoot a manned projectile from a giant cannon.

Curiously, the initial mission concept, if not the hardware, followed closely the direct-shot idea of the science fiction writers. By January, 1961, two routes to the moon seemed feasible—a direct-ascent trajectory using large Nove-type launch vehicles and orbit-rendezvous techniques using Saturn-type boosters.

At that time, a number of large aircraft firms began feasibility studies to determine what a moonship should look like. Krafft A. Ehricke, program director for Centaur, the nation's first hydrogen-powered space vehicle at General Dynamics/Astronautics, conceived of a tubular-shaped lunar reconnaissance vehicle powered by a low-thrust engine burning hydrogen and oxygen, to be followed by a three-stage chemical rocket burning oxygen and kerosene in the first stage of 1.5 million pounds thrust.

A fellow engineer, Freeman D'Vincent, conceived of a lunar lander not unlike Apollo's LM, with a glider-like earth reentry vehicle poised on top.

General Electric went a step further, to propose a hemispheric Polar Moon Base from which lunar exploration vehicles could venture.

Martin's moonship was a direct-ascent rocket, in which man's role would be that of reliability, maintenance, control and decision-making.

Douglas engineers saw no reason why a huge nuclear-powered space vehicle could not shuttle back and forth between earth and moon ferrying astronauts and supplies in support of a huge shell-like "Sun Dome," in which solar energy provided heat, light and power for the pressurized home away from home.

All these were exotic, uninhibited concepts, and they remained just that. Not until President Kennedy's challenge to industry did Apollo Project actually get moving, and then only because a team of engineers at North American Aviation considered the challenge their meat. On that team were such men as Charles Feltz, Chief Engineer, who had won attention as designer of the world's fastest airplane, the rocket ship X-15.

More than 100 engineers pitched in to design an Apollo moonship and on November 28, 1961, North American walked off with the Apollo contract, beating out 11 competitors. By January, 1962, the big race was on. Russia already was the big favorite for getting to the moon first. If America was to win the contest, lights would have to burn late at night.

As originally proposed in the initial Requests For

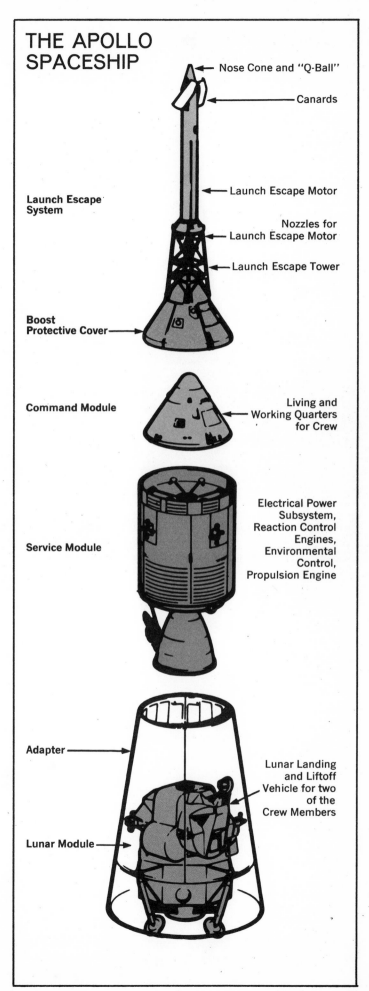

THE APOLLO SPACESHIP

Nose Cone and "Q-Ball"

Canards

Launch Escape System

Launch Escape Motor

Nozzles for Launch Escape Motor

Launch Escape Tower

Boost Protective Cover

Command Module

Living and Working Quarters for Crew

Service Module

Electrical Power Subsystem, Reaction Control Engines, Environmental Control, Propulsion Engine

Adapter

Lunar Landing and Liftoff Vehicle for two of the Crew Members

Lunar Module

COMMAND MODULE

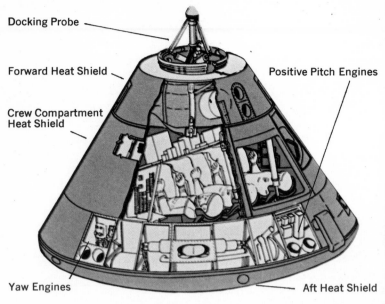

- Docking Probe
- Forward Heat Shield
- Crew Compartment Heat Shield
- Positive Pitch Engines
- Yaw Engines
- Aft Heat Shield

Command Module (CM) Structure — The basic structure of the command module is a pressure vessel encased in heat-shields, cone-shaped 12 feet high, base diameter of 12 feet 10 inches, and launch weight 12,405 pounds. The command module consists of the forward compartment which contains two negative pitch reaction control engines and components of the Earth landing system; the crew compartment, or inner pressure vessel, containing crew accommodations, controls and displays, and spacecraft systems; and the aft compartment housing ten reaction control engines and propellant tankage.

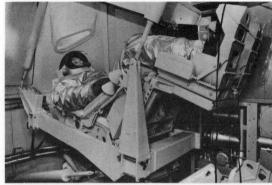

TYPICAL CROSS-SECTION OF CREW COMPARTMENT HEAT SHIELD AND INNER STRUCTURE

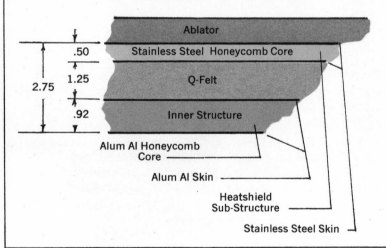

- Ablator
- Stainless Steel Honeycomb Core
- .50
- Q-Felt
- 1.25
- 2.75
- Inner Structure
- .92
- Alum Al Honeycomb Core
- Alum Al Skin
- Heatshield Sub-Structure
- Stainless Steel Skin

SERVICE MODULE

Service Module (SM) Structure — The service module is a cylinder 12 feet 10 inches in diameter by 22 feet long. It weighs 36,159 pounds at launch. Aluminum honeycomb panes one inch thick form the outer skin, and milled aluminum radial beams separate the interior into six sections containing service propulsion system and reaction control fuel-oxidizer tankage, fuel cells, cryogenic oxygen and hydrogen, and onboard consumables.

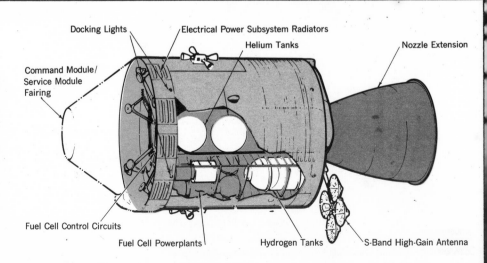

- Docking Lights
- Electrical Power Subsystem Radiators
- Helium Tanks
- Nozzle Extension
- Command Module/ Service Module Fairing
- Fuel Cell Control Circuits
- Fuel Cell Powerplants
- Hydrogen Tanks
- S-Band High-Gain Antenna

LUNAR MODULE

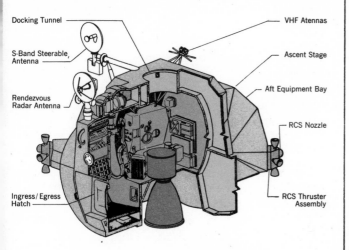

- Docking Tunnel
- S-Band Steerable Antenna
- Rendezvous Radar Antenna
- Ingress/Egress Hatch
- VHF Atennas
- Ascent Stage
- Aft Equipment Bay
- RCS Nozzle
- RCS Thruster Assembly

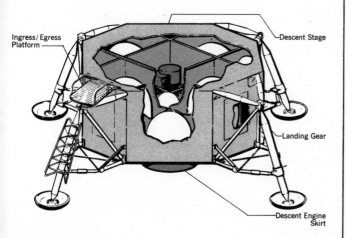

- Ingress/Egress Platform
- Descent Stage
- Landing Gear
- Descent Engine Skirt

The Lunar Module (LM) is a two-stage vehicle designed for space operations near and on the Moon. The LM is incapable of reentering the atmosphere and is, in effect, a true spacecraft. Joined by four explosive bolts and umbilicals, the ascent and descent stages of the LM operate as a unit until staging, when the ascent stage functions as a single spacecraft for rendezvous and docking with the CSM.

Proposals, NASA wanted a moonship that could be boosted by a Saturn V rocket on a direct-ascent trajectory to hit the moon the way a duck shooter wings his target, by simply firing a little ahead and letting the duck fly into the shot.

Early success with solid propellants indicated to NASA that they would be best for blasting off from the moon on the return trip to earth, and so the first Apollo engineering order called for this combination; a direct ascent and a solid-fuel liftoff for the return trip.

Then, in April, 1962 an obscure scientist at NASA's Langley Research Center came up with a different idea, so far out he was laughed at. Dr. John C. Houbolt stuck to his guns and pushed his concept, called LOR (Lunar Orbit Rendezvous). For the skeptics he drew diagrams on a blackboard, showing morphologically that LOR offered a choice of many different ways of reaching the moon. He was fortunately believed, and on July 11, NASA disclosed plans for development of a two-man excursion module in which astronauts could separate from the lunar-orbiting command module and land independently, later returning to hook up again in lunar orbit and go home.

The lunar excursion module became known as the LEM, and later LM for short. Grumman Aircraft won the contract to design and build it, and at North American engineers began redesigning Apollo for its newly assigned role. Included were a new service module and adapter design, plus revisions to the command module to incorporate LEM rendezvous and docking capability. By late 1962, things were finally humming.

At North American's Space & Information Division at Downey, California, a final assembly line was established to turn out the vast number of Apollo spacecraft needed for the huge program. There had to be boilerplate models for ocean drop tests and recovery training; mockups to lay out the maze of life support and other systems inside the command module; test capsules to be tortured with heat and cold and incredible stresses to insure that the final product would survive a ride through the hostile environment of cislunar space and the moon landing itself.

From the top down, Apollo evolved as a strikingly beautiful and sophisticated vehicle, perhaps the most ingenious ever built by man. From the Q-Ball nose cone atop the launch escape tower to the bell-shaped service propulsion engine nozzle underneath the moonship, everything essential to a trip to our celestial satellite and back was there, the product of hundreds of subcontractors in every state who poured their skill and energies into the grand national effort.

Apollo consists of three basic parts—the command module, the service module and the lunar module—topped by the launch escape system for all missions. Two models of Apollo were designed—the

Block I model for earth-orbit missions, the Block II model for lunar missions with the LM added.

Heart of the moonship is the Command Module, providing living, working and leisure-time quarters for the three-man crew. It consists of two shells; a honeycomb sandwich of stainless steel covered with ablative material, making up a heat shield, and an inner shell of aluminum honeycomb between aluminum alloy sheets. Both shells are separated by a double layer of micro-quartz fiber insulation. Light and rugged, this double shell provides about the same room per occupant as a compact car, plus an efficiently laid out combination office, cockpit, laboratory, radio station, kitchen, bedroom, bathroom and den.

Air conditioned to a comfortable 75 degrees, the cabin provides a shirtsleeve environment in which astronauts breathe a complex system of two gases, oxygen and nitrogen. In the CM are controls for guidance during flight, test equipment to monitor spacecraft systems, television, telemetry and tracking equipment and two-way radios to stay in constant contact with earth and among astronauts during moon exploration and lunar orbit rendezvous. These and other pieces of equipment, for such delicate maneuvers as the earth landing, take up almost every available inch of module space.

Though able to move about from one station to another, most of the crew time is spent reclining weightless in contour couches, resting on crushable honeycomb shock struts to absorb landing impact forces.

Beneath the Command Module sits the Service Module (SM), housing the electrical power system, reaction control engines and part of the environmental control system, as well as the main propulsion engine for earth return and midcourse correction.

Constructed mainly of aluminum alloy, the SM carries propellants stored in six wedged segments surrounding the main engine. It remains attached to the CM until just prior to earth entry, when it is jettisoned to burn up in the atmosphere.

Tucked away inside a conical "orange peel" aluminum spacecraft-LM adapter (to protect it during launch) is the weird, buglike Lunar Module (LM), a 16-ton vehicle that has been called the first true spaceship. It is designed to function only in the vacuum of space. This is the "bug" advocated by Dr. Houbolt to make possible the Lunar Orbit Rendezvous technique (LOR), a concept actually first proposed by a Russian mechanic, Yuri Kondratyuk, half a century ago.

LM consists of two basic sections, the ascent stage and the descent stage. The ascent stage houses the crew compartment, ascent engine and propellant tanks and all crew controls. It also provides shelter and a base of operations for the two LM crewmen who actually visit the moon, leaving the third astronaut orbiting the moon in the CSM (Command and Service Modules).

The descent stage, consisting primarily of the descent engine, propellant tanks and landing gear assembly, also houses batteries, storage space for scientific gadgets to use on the moon, extra oxygen, water and helium tanks. This stage serves as the launch platform for the ascent stage, for return to rendezvous and docking with the CSM after the historic landing on the moon's surface. Once back inside the Command Module, the astronauts jettison the ascent stage to remain in orbit around the moon while they head back to earth.

The design appeared beautiful on the drawing boards and all systems checked out perfectly during the long months of engineering and fabrication and testing, but would they all work together in space? The way to find out was to send an unmanned Apollo spacecraft up and see what happened.

No crash program such as Apollo runs entirely smoothly, and while American ingenuity brought the project along more rapidly than had been hoped for, setbacks dogged Apollo almost from the start. On September 6, 1963, Apollo Command Module BP-3 was destroyed during parachute tests at El Centro, California, when the third canopy failed to deploy.

On January 8, 1964, President Johnson reiterated the late President Kennedy's call for "an expedition to the moon in this decade, in cooperation with other powers if possible, alone if necessary."

It did not prove possible to share the moon voyage with Russia, hence America got on with the job, and in mid-February a boilerplate Apollo Command Module BP-13 was shipped to Cape Kennedy for the first orbit test. BP-13 flew on May 28, the first Apollo vehicle to go into orbit.

From that day forward, Apollo test spacecraft went up with increasing regularity from Cape Kennedy and from White Sands Proving Ground in New Mexico to check out all systems. All these were either mockup or boilerplate moonships, until on October 20, 1965 the first actual Apollo spacecraft SC-009, was accepted from North American by NASA and shipped off to the spaceport in Florida.

On February 26, 1966 SC-009 was lofted into space atop a Saturn 1B launch vehicle, the first flight of an unmanned Apollo CSM, to check its ability to withstand reentry temperatures. The flight was successful. Six months later, Apollo Space Craft 011 rocketed into space in a second test of reentry capability under high heat load.

The time was drawing near when the moonship would be man-rated. All seemed to go well until at 0200 universal time on January 11, 1967 nature herself struck without warning. At that moment a monstrous flare erupted from the sun, sending toward earth the most violent interplanetary storm ever recorded.

Five orbiting scientific satellites reported the

approach of the solar wind's shock front as it distorted the earth's magnetosphere to the lowest altitude ever recorded. Scientists asked: could Apollo astronauts survive such a storm?

Sixteen days later tragedy struck the Apollo program with devastating suddenness, not in space but on a launch pad at Cape Kennedy during a routine ground test. Fire erupted inside the moonship, taking the lives of Lt. Col. Virgil I. Grissom, Lt. Col. Edward H. White and Lt. Commander Roger B. Chaffee.

A thorough review of Project Apollo caused a six-month time slip in the tight launch schedule and resulted in extensive redesign and modification of the Command Module, including the escape hatch, materials, earth landing system, cabin repressurization and protective coverings for plumbing and wiring.

By November 7, 1967, the race was on again, with launch of Apollo 4, during which the monster rocket Saturn V was first used as a moonship booster. After a high, looping flight, Apollo 4 streaked back into the atmosphere at 25,000 mph, a lunar return speed that created a blistering 5,000°F heat.

On January 22, 1968, a LM was first tested in flight aboard Apollo 5, and after a final unmanned flight by Apollo 6 on April 4, the moonship was ready for man-rating. Apollo 7 went up from the Cape October 11, 1968 with a three-man crew, the first spaceflight of U.S. astronauts since the final Gemini flight two years earlier.

A Saturn 1B flawlessly placed Apollo 7 in orbit. Crew commander was veteran astronaut Walter M. Schirra, Jr. With him were Donn Eisele and Walter Cunningham, making their first space flight. The 11-day mission, highly successful, showed that the moonship was ready for the long 231,000-mile voyage to the moon and back.

Apollo 8, flown by command pilot Frank Borman, James Lovell, Jr., and William Anders, at last streaked for the moon on December 21, atop a Saturn V rocket in a flight now historic.

In seven years American spacemen had reached to the moon and beyond; the time was ready for a final checkout of the LM, in a flight to within 50,000 feet of the lunar surface in May, 1969. The final step, putting an American astronaut on the moon itself in mid-July, completed President Kennedy's assignment.

That fateful journey must stand, in fact, not as the end of giant space exploration effort but as only the beginning. In all, Apollo had reached its goal with a total of 49 manned or test spacecraft and service modules, 30 boilerplate vehicles and 23 full-scale mockups, in addition to numerous other support hardware items. Thus Apollo stands as a miracle of American technology in opening the way toward future exploration of the moon and the distant planets by earthmen.

Development of Apollo Spacesuits.

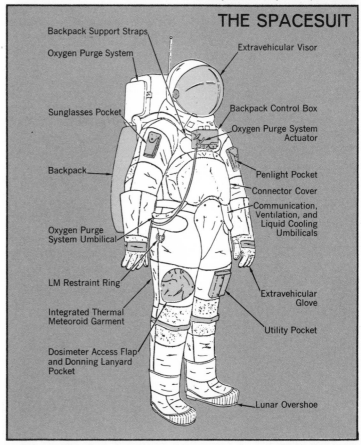

THE SPACESUIT

Backpack Support Straps

Oxygen Purge System

Extravehicular Visor

Sunglasses Pocket

Backpack Control Box

Oxygen Purge System Actuator

Backpack

Penlight Pocket

Connector Cover

Communication, Ventilation, and Liquid Cooling Umbilicals

Oxygen Purge System Umbilical

LM Restraint Ring

Extravehicular Glove

Integrated Thermal Meteoroid Garment

Utility Pocket

Dosimeter Access Flap and Donning Lanyard Pocket

Lunar Overshoe

MISSION PROFILE

Apollo missions are of two distinct categories: earth-orbital and lunar. Each is designed as a specific phase of flight testing for the spacecraft, the launch vehicles, launch and communications equipment and procedures and crew operations. While the actual landing of two Americans on the moon is the most dramatic portion of the complex experiment, the entire program has been a classic example of dedication. All the planning and work that has gone before has been aimed at one goal: placing Americans on another celestial body.

For planning purposes, the lunar mission is divided into phases, each phase vital, even critical, to the successful completion of the flight. The first Moon landing is a typical mission, broken down on an optimum timeline through the following pages.

BY LEROI SMITH

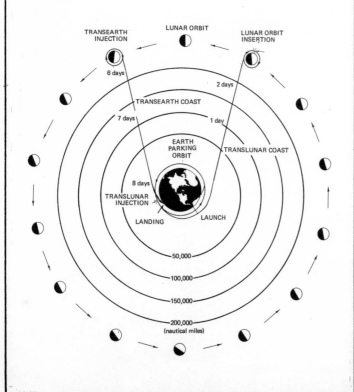

LAUNCH / TIME 0.0 HOURS

The Apollo spacecraft is hurled into space from Cape Kennedy aboard a Saturn V rocket weighing 3000 tons. The rocket first stage builds up a total thrust of 7.5 million pounds before the vehicle is released from the launch pad. The first stage burns for about 2½ minutes and reaches a velocity of about 5400 miles per hour up to an altitude of about 40 miles. When the F-1 engines (first engines used) cut off, retrorockets on the first stage fire to separate first and second stages of the rocket vehicle. Four seconds later, the second stage (with five J-2 engines) ignites and boosts the spacecraft to an altitude of approximately 114 miles. The second stage engines work for about six minutes, increasing velocity of the craft to 15,000 mph, then the second stage is also jettisoned.

The third stage J-2 engine starts at separation from the second stage and burns for about two minutes again increasing speed to about 16,500 mph. This puts the spacecraft into a near-circular earth orbit about 115 miles above the ground. During the ascent, the crew monitors the launch vehicle displays in case a mission abort is necessary; relays boost and general craft information to the ground; and watches the critical subsystem displays. All this information is contained on the big instrument panel in the cockpit.

Special aircraft monitor Apollo.   **Electronic displays at Houston.**

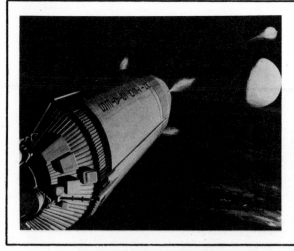

EARTH PARKING ORBIT / TIME 0.2 HOURS

At a speed of about 17,400 miles per hour, the spacecraft is placed in the "parking" orbit about 100 miles above the ground. The craft will circle the earth up to three times if necessary, to get the perfect timing for Translunar Injection (TLI), which means it could stay in earth orbit up to 4½ hours. All subsystems are checked again during this time, and because injection (TLI) is desirable as soon as possible after checkout, the craft will probably head for the moon on the second earth orbit. To inject the spacecraft into TLI, the crew ignites the third-stage engine.

Moon over Pacific Ocean.

TRANSLUNAR INJECTION / TIME 3.1 HOURS

The guidance system in the third stage tells the rocket engine exactly when to ignite and how long to burn. This means the engine will run for about 6½ minutes, which increases the speed from 17,400 mph to 24,300 mph, the velocity needed to leave the earth parking orbit and enter a trajectory to the moon. This trajectory is usually one that gives "free return." If the craft doesn't achieve moon orbit, it will return to earth.

Escape from the earth must occur at the correct point to cause the spacecraft's trajectory to cross in front of the moon. The anticipated intercept of the moon path will occur after about three days flight and at an altitude of about 80 nautical miles above the moon. During engine thrusting for TLI, the crew remain in the couches and monitor the main instrument displays.

Third stage fires Apollo out of earth orbit.

4 LM TRANSFER AND DOCKING / TIME 3.5 HOURS

For the next sixty or so hours, the spacecraft is in Translunar Coast, headed toward the moon with no further engine firing to gain speed. During this time there are a number of vital missions to be performed. First of these is moving the LM (Lunar Module) to the front of the CSM (Command and Service Modules).

The crewmen move their couches to see out the docking windows and the craft commander begins the transposition and docking maneuver by firing the service module reaction control engines. The commander stops the CSM 50 to 75 feet from the third stage, turns 180 degrees with a pitch maneuver so the docking windows are facing the LM, rolls the CSM for alignment, and then makes the docking. Pressure between CSM and LM is equalized and all latches are checked. After docking, the spacecraft is separated from the third stage by spring thrusters.

MID-COURSE CORRECTIONS / TIME 12.7 HOURS

As the spacecraft travels along the programmed trajectory, gravitational pull from the earth will slow it from 25,000 mph to 2,386 mph. When it enters the moon's gravitational pull, the speed will accelerate to 5,200 mph.

Shortly after the coasting begins, the spacecraft is oriented for navigation sightings of stars and earth landmarks. The craft is also put into a slow roll of about two revolutions an hour to provide uniform solar heating.

If the ground tracking stations show a course correction is needed, it is done early in the flight so the corrections will still be of small magnitude. The solar heating revolutions are stopped for course corrections.

During the trip to the moon, the crew has many special duties to perform relative to the spacecraft. They eat in shifts but sleep at the same time. Ground control monitors the spacecraft all the time and can awaken the crew if necessary. Final mid-course corrections come at 61 hours if needed.

CSM separates from LM stage, is turned 180° and two units docked.

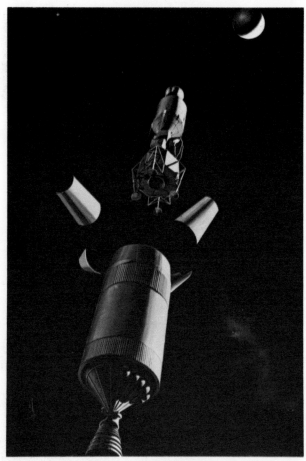

CSM and LM continue to moon.

LUNAR ORBIT INSERTION / TIME 64.3 HOURS

Insertion of the craft into lunar orbit (LOI) is really just a matter of braking from about 5200 mph to 3600 mph as the vehicle swings behind the moon. Retrograde braking rockets do the slowing, and are programmed to work on control from Mission Control Center in Houston, Texas. During the retro firing, the spacecraft is out of communication with the ground as it is behind the moon and radio contact (which requires line-of-sight transmission) is lost for about 45 minutes of the 2-hour lunar orbit.

During the Lunar Orbit Coast, all the systems are checked and double-checked, with fine alignments made in navigational procedures. After the commander and LM pilot transfer to the LM, they perform a long series of LM subsystem checks. After this checkout, which comes at 67 hours, the LM is separated from the Command Module. The LM and CM move apart slightly so the CM pilot can inspect the LM landing gear. The CM will remain in lunar orbit for about a day and a half until the LM returns from the moon. During this time, the CM pilot is extremely busy monitoring communications between earth and the LM and assisting in many other parts of LM maneuvering.

LM and CSM orbit moon together, then LM descends to surface and leaves CSM in orbit.

LM moves away from Command Module.

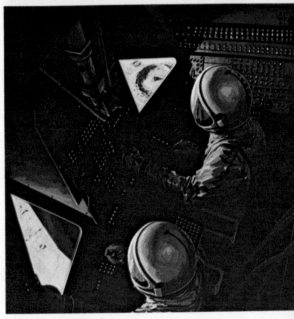

LM crew studies moon for landing site.

LUNAR MODULE DESCENT / TIME 68.4 HOURS

The descent engine will put the LM into an elliptical orbit that comes within 50,000 feet of the moon. Near this low point, the rocket will fire again, braking the module speed further. The LM crew is very busy at this time with velocity checks, sub-system checks, landing radar test, altitude maneuvering, and preparation of the LM computer. The landing area is scheduled north between 5 degrees and 5 degrees south of the moon equator and plus 45 degrees to minus 45 degrees in longitude, or an area about 200 miles wide and 1500 miles long. The exact touchdown location must be determined by such current factors as terrain, lighting, and fuel required for ascent and rendezvous.

The landing maneuvers will take about eight minutes, or at about 69.4 hours into the flight. Speed will drop from about 3600 mph to zero. The final approach starts at about 9000 feet and is controlled by computer until the craft is about 500 feet off the ground, then the commander takes over. Immediately upon touchdown the commander shuts off the descent engine.

Below — Eight suitable man landing sites were originally selected for the Apollo 11 flight, the number later trimmed to five and finally three. Site 2 in the Sea of Tranquility was the ultimate target, missed by only four miles because of unknown rocks at the scheduled touchdown point.

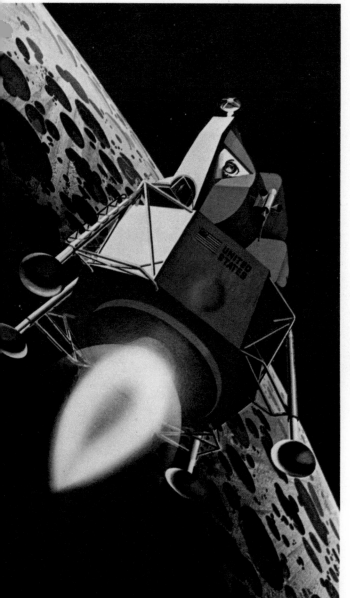

LM commander flies unit to touchdown.

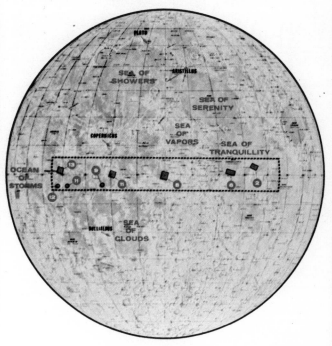

The commander and LM pilot will stay in the lunar module for about 4½ hours checking out the ascent stage of the vehicle and the extravehicular mobility units. The LM cabin is depressurized and the commander descends the LM ladder in his special spacesuit. The commander gets samples of moon surface material and transfers this to the LM pilot, who has been filming the process. After the LM pilot has handed out special scientific equipment, he joins the commander. The commander will probably stay outside about three hours, the LM pilot about two hours. The astronauts will closely inspect the LM exterior, set up S-band surface antenna, collect a preliminary set of geological samples, and make a TV scan of the landing site.

A second exploration of the moon surface may follow a brief period of sleep and will also last about three hours. They will have many things to do, including taking more geological samples, photography, exploration of the surface (astronauts will be restricted to close proximity of the LM), and setting up the scientific station that will send data back to earth after the astronauts leave. Time on the moon will be around 22 hours.

Astronauts set up scientific instruments.

7

Actual landing site will be relatively smooth.

LM ascent stage uses leg platform as launching pad.

LM ascent stage uses leg platform as launching pad.

The two astronauts will be launched into lunar orbit in the ascending (upper) section of the LM. The lower "leg" section of the LM will be the launch pad. After about seven minutes, the engine will have the LM coasting into an orbit with the Command Module.

Once in orbit, the LM takes about 30 minutes to intercept the Command Module, with course corrections made by the computer. The commander takes over for final docking. During lunar orbit the commander and LM pilot transfer all the collected moon data and samples to the CM. The LM is then jettisoned and the crew is ready for return to earth.

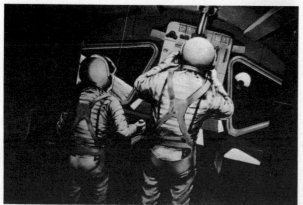

Docking LM and CM.

Astronauts walk between LM and CM if mission dictates.

TRANS EARTH INJECTION / TIME 109.1 HOURS

With information transmitted from Mission Control Center, the proper injection into TEI is accomplished. For this, the Command Service Module engine fires for about 2½ minutes to increase spacecraft velocity to about 5500 mph. This is a critical maneuver, as it takes place behind the moon, out of communication with the earth. Communication is regained about 20 minutes after the engine has cut off.

The coasting trip back to earth will last from 80 to 110 hours. The spacecraft velocity gradually decreases because of the moon's gravitational pull, then it increases to about 25,000 mph when it enters the earth atmosphere. The trip back to earth is similar to the trip outbound, except that about four hours before re-entry, the Command Service Module is rotated to cool the CM shield in shadow.

At about 195 hours into the mission, the final course corrections will be made if necessary. The course angle at this stage is extremely critical: if too steep, the heat build-up will be too great; if too shallow, the craft can skip off the atmosphere like a flat rock off a lake. Shortly before entry, the Service Module is jettisoned.

9

CM heads for home by firing rocket engine on moon far side.

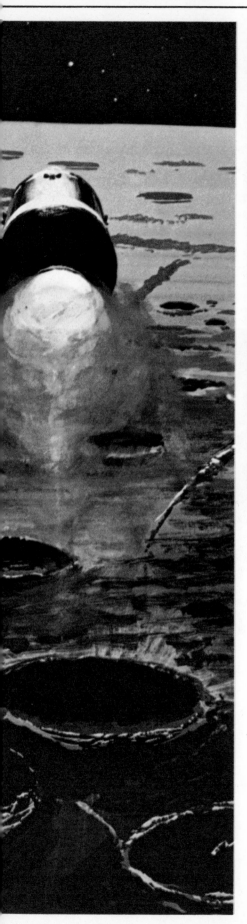

Mid-course corrections are vital.
Below — the earth as only space travelers know it.

ENTRY / TIME 198.3 HOURS

At a speed of about 25,000 mph and an altitude of 400,000 feet, the CM begins to encounter atmosphere resistance. The blunt side of the CM is facing forward, where the heat build-up may reach 5000 degrees F. Despite this intense heat, inside the spacecraft the temperature is controlled at 80 degrees. Maximum gravitational forces felt by the crew will be a bit over 5 G's.

At 198.4 hours into the mission, the drogue chutes are deployed at about 25,000 feet (after the forward heat shield is jettisoned). The drogues are only half-opened at first and then open fully, slowing the CM from 325 mph to about 125 mph. At about 10,700 feet the drogues are released and the main parachutes are deployed to slow the craft to about 22 mph. Final descent on the main parachutes takes about five minutes.

On re-entry, CM separates from service module and turns blunt heat shield toward atmosphere.

Earth touchdown is scheduled to be in the Pacific within plus/minus 35 degrees latitude and 165 degrees W. longitude. Recovery forces which practice for such flight returns constantly will pick up the returning astronauts from the floating Command Module. The spacecraft crew will remain in special quarantine facilities until 21 days from lunar liftoff, while medical specialists check them thoroughly.

Parachutes slow CM.

CM floats in ocean.

Frogmen assist triumphant space crew.

Crew is returned to aircraft carrier.

...FOR ALL MANKIND

Edwin E. Aldrin, Jr.
Lunar Module Pilot

Michael Collins
Command Module Pilot

Neil A. Armstrong
Commander

THE EAGLE HAS LANDED

CAPCOM - Eagle you're looking great, coming up 9 minutes.

PAO - We're now in the approach phase of it, looking good. Altitude 52 hundred feet.

EAGLE - Manual auto attitude control is good.

CAPCOM - Roger, copy.

PAO - Altitude 42 hundred—

CAPCOM - Roger, copy.

PAO - Altitude 4200.

CAPCOM - Houston. You're go for landing. Over.

EAGLE - Roger, understand. Go for landing. 3000 feet.

CAPCOM - Copy.

EAGLE - 12 alarm. 1201.

EAGLE - 1201.

CAPCOM - Roger. 1201 alarm.

EAGLE - We're go. Hang tight. We're go. 2,000 feet. 2,000 feet into the AGS. 47 degrees.

CAPCOM - Roger.

EAGLE - 47 degrees.

CAPCOM - Eagle looking great. You're go.

PAO - Altitude 1600. 1400 feet. Still looking very good.

CAPCOM - Roger. 1202. We copy it.

EAGLE - 35 degrees. 35 degrees. 750, coming down at 23. 700 feet, 21 down. 33 degrees. 600 feet, down at 19. 540 feet, down at 30—down at 15. 400 feet, down at 9. (garbled) 8 forward. 350, down at 4. 330, 3½ down. We're pegged on horizontal velocity. 300 feet, down 3½. 47 forward. (garbled) Down 1 a minute. 1½ down. 70. Got the shadow out there. 50, down at 2½. 19 forward. Altitude-velocity lights. 3½ down, 220 feet. 13 forward. 11 forward, coming down nicely. 200 feet, 4½ down. 5½ down. 160, 6½ down, 5½ down, 9 forward. 5 percent. Quantity light. 75 feet, things looking good. Down a half. 6 forward.

CAPCOM - 60 seconds.

EAGLE - Lights on. Down 2½. Forward. Forward. Good. 40 feet, down 2½. Picking up some dust. 30 feet, 2½ down. Faint shadow. 4 forward. 4 forward, drifting to the right a little. 6 (garbled) down a half.

CAPCOM - 30 seconds.

EAGLE - (garbled) forward. Drifting right. (garbled) Contact light. Okay, engine stop. ACA out of detent. Modes control both auto, descent engine command override, off. Engine arm, off. 413 is in.

CAPCOM - We copy you down, Eagle.

EAGLE - (Armstrong) Houston, Tranquility base here. The Eagle has landed.

CAPCOM - Roger, Tranquility, we copy you on the ground. You've got a bunch of guys about to turn blue. We're breathing again. Thanks a lot.

ONE SMALL STEP FOR MAN.
A GIANT LEAP FOR MANKIND

ARMSTRONG -

As the—The surface is fine and powdery. I can—I can pick it up loosely with my toe. It does adhere in fine layers like powdered charcoal to the sole and sides of my boots. I only go in a small fraction of an inch. Maybe an eighth of an inch, but I can see the footprints of my boots and the treads in the fine sandy particles.

CAPCOM - Okay, Neil, we can see you coming down the ladder now.

ARMSTRONG - Okay, I just checked—getting back up to that first step, Buzz, it's not even collapsed too far, but it's adequate to get back up.

CAPCOM - Roger, we copy.

ARMSTRONG - It takes a pretty good little jump.

CAPCOM - Buzz, this is Houston. F 2 1/160th second for shadow photography on the sequence camera.

ALDRIN - Okay.

ARMSTRONG - I'm at the foot of the ladder. The LM foot pads are only depressed in the surface about 1 or 2 inches. Although the surface appears to be very, very fine grained, as you get close to it. It's almost like a powder. Now and then, it's very fine.

ARMSTRONG - I'm going to step off the LM now.

ARMSTRONG - That's one small step for man. One giant leap for mankind.

Prime mission of Apollo 11 was simply to perform a manned lunar landing and return. While man had long dreamed of walking on another celestial body, anything more than a brief evaluation of the alien terrain would have to wait for the ten Apollos to follow.

When Commander Neal Armstrong took control of the LM and landed it safely beyond the programmed target, he came to rest west of the prime Site No. 2 (latitude .0799° north, longitude 23.46° east). Man's first assault of his neighboring satellite was about 20 miles southwest of the crater Maskelyne, which is on the right side of the Moon as viewed from Earth. Immediately upon landing, the crew prepared the assent stage for take off before attempting the Moon walk.

As Armstrong set foot on the Moon, he uttered the immortal phrase, "That's one small step for man, one giant leap for mankind," referring to the fact that man had at last made a physical conquest in space. This step was televised across the hundreds of thousands of miles, which allowed millions of Earth bound citizens to also participate in the great adventure. More than a flight to our closest neighbor, it was a triumph for modern technology. It proved that man is limited in achievement only by desire.

Crude as this flight will appear to future generations, history will record Apollo 11 as one of the most remarkable achievements of all time.

MAGNIFICENT DESOLATION

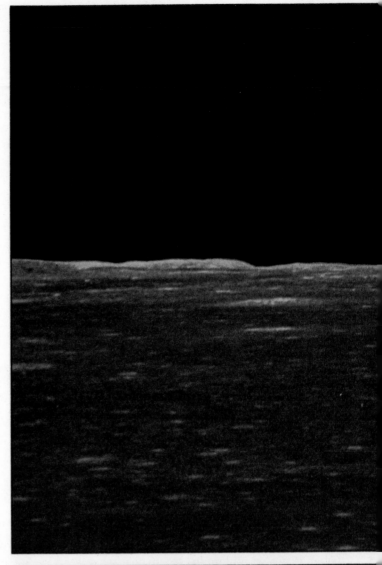

ALDRIN - Now, I want to back up and partially close the hatch. Making sure not to lock it on my way out.

ARMSTRONG - A good thought.

ALDRIN - That's our home for the next couple of hours and I want to take good care of it. Okay, I'm on the top step and I can look down over the RCU, landing gear pads. That's a very simple matter to hop down from one step to the next.

ARMSTRONG - Yes, I found it to be very comfortable and walking is also very comfortable. You've got three more steps and then a long one.

ALDRIN - Okay, I'm going to leave that one foot up there and both hands down to about the fourth rung up.

ARMSTRONG - There you go.

ALDRIN - Okay. Now I think I'll do the same.

ARMSTRONG - A little more. About another inch. There you got it. That's a good step. About a three footer.

ALDRIN - Beautiful, beautiful.

ARMSTRONG - Isn't that something. Magnificent sight down here.

ALDRIN - Magnificent desolation.

What astronauts Armstrong and Aldrin saw was awesome. Stark. Outstanding and marked contrast. Total desolation. Neither hostile or inviting. The Moon appeared like much of the western U.S. desert.

The lunar surface is mountainous and crater-pitted, the mountains rising to 12,000 feet in height. The Moon's back side is almost all craters with only smooth areas facing the earth; "Seas" covered with a layer of fine grained material resemble powdered sands or dust. The LM pad sank only about 2", while the astronauts reported high defined boot prints only 1/8" deep.

There is no air, no wind, and no moisture on the Moon. Temperature ranges from 243° during the two-week day to 279° below zero in the night. Armstrong reported a definite temperature variation when moving into the LM shadow. Only about 1/4 Earth size, the horizon showed a definite curvature. Aldrin reported a lack of any general color.

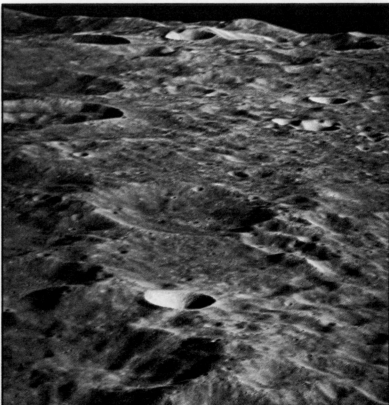

YES.
THIS IS HISTORY

COLUMBIA - Yes. This is History. Yes. Read you loud and clear. How's it going?

CAPCOM - Roger. The EVA is progressing beautifully. I believe they are setting up the flag now.

COLUMBIA - Great.

CAPCOM - I guess you're about the only person around that doesn't have TV coverage of the scene.

COLUMBIA - That's right. That's all right. I don't mind a bit. How is the quality of the TV?

CAPCOM - Oh, it's beautiful, Mike. Really is.

COLUMBIA - Oh, gee, that's great. Is the lighting half way decent?

CAPCOM - Yes, indeed. They've got the flag up and you can see the stars and stripes on the lunar surface.

COLUMBIA - Beautiful. Just beautiful.

CAPCOM - Neil and Buzz, the President of the United States is in his office now and would like to say a few words to you. Over.

ARMSTRONG - That would be an honor.

CAPCOM - Go ahead Mr. President, this is Houston. Out.

PRES NIXON - Neil and Buzz, I am talking to you by telephone from the Oval Room at the White House. And this certainly has to be the most historic telephone call ever made. I just can't tell you how proud we all are of what you . . . for every American, this has to be the proudest day of our lives. And for people all over the world, I am sure they, too, join with Americans, in recognizing what a feat this is. Because of what you have done, the heavens have become a part of man's world. And as you talk to us from the Sea of Tranquility, it inspires us to double our efforts to bring peace and tranquility to earth. For one priceless moment, in the whole history of man, all the people on this earth are truly one. One in their pride in what you have done. And one in our prayers, that you will return safely to earth.

ARMSTRONG - Thank you, Mr. President. It's a great honor and privilege for us to be here representing not only the United States but men of peace of all nations. And with interest and a curiosity and a vision for the future. It's an honor for us to be able to participate here today.

Apollo 11 could do what no other space flights have been able to accomplish: visit the Moon and get human observations of what was found. However, there were many scientific experiments designated essential to the mission. EASEP, the Early Apollo Scientific Experiment Package, included a lasar ranging retro-reflector to measure the exact distance between the Earth and the Moon for the first time and a passive seismic experiment package for measuring shock and vibration of the lunar surface which will help to determine the general structure of the lunar core. While on the Moon, Armstrong and Aldrin used still and motion picture cameras to record their activities. While the astronauts gathered rocks and soil, a solar wind composition flag was unfurled to entrap particles, gases and other selected elements. As the astronauts neared the end of their Moon walk, everything was stowed in the rocket for return to Earth and to eager scientists the world over. During the little more than two-hour Moon walk, Armstrong and Aldrin experienced no ill effect from the 1/6 gravity force.

Here men from the planet Earth
first set foot upon the Moon
July 1969, A.D.

WE CAME IN PEACE FOR ALL MANKIND

Like something straight from Buck Rogers, ground support tracking equipment gives scientists and engineers precise information on spacecraft.

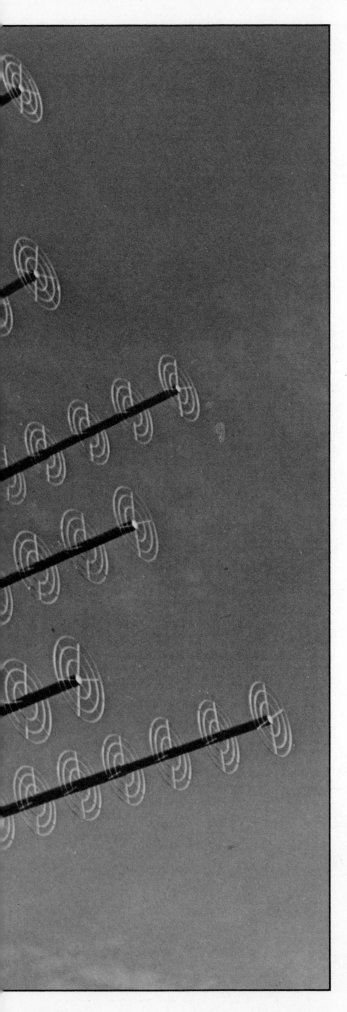

GROUND SUPPORT

BY PETER ABBOTT

At approximately 10 o'clock Eastern Standard Time on Christmas Eve, 1968, the strong, clear voice of Air Force Captain Frank Borman, astronaut, spoke quietly to the people of planet Earth from the region of the moon, across 231,000 miles of space:

"Apollo Eight has a message for you."

Then, solemnly, came the now-historic, emotion-packed reading of Genesis by Major William A. Anders, Captain James A. Lovell, Jr., and Captain Borman.

"In the beginning," Major Anders' voice intoned, "God created the Heaven and the Earth . . . "

Across planet Earth that night, people sat by their television sets and radios and listened, many moved to tears by the spiritual beauty of the unforgettable moment. Though the impact of the message itself was remarkable, few who listened could adequately appreciate the incredible technological achievement the Christmas Eve reading represented. It is one thing to have something important to say, another to say it, communicating across the wilderness of space and into the homes of hundreds of millions of people, as if the astronauts were in the very same room.

Back in 1945, twelve years before Russia's earth-orbiting Sputnik I heralded the dawn of the Space Age on October 4, 1957, a British science writer named Arthur C. Clarke was considered a visionary when he predicted that communications satellites would soon be broadcasting scientific information back to earth.

In that same year, 1945, all doubt was finally removed that the earth's ionosphere might constitute an electronic barrier, preventing communica-

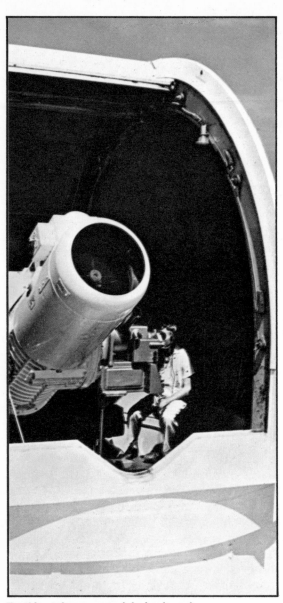

Tracking telescope used during launch.

Manned Spacecraft Center, Houston, Texas.

Tracking ship USNS Mercury, used for Apollo.

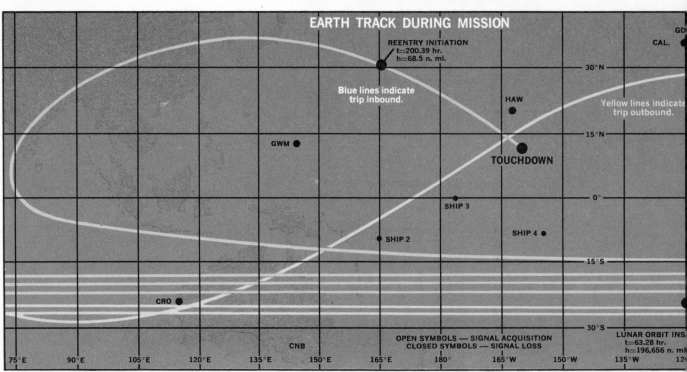

EARTH TRACK DURING MISSION

REENTRY INITIATION
t=200.39 hr.
h=68.5 n. mi.

GD

CAL.

Blue lines indicate
trip inbound.

HAW

Yellow lines indicate
trip outbound.

15° N

GWM

TOUCHDOWN

30° N

0°

SHIP 3

SHIP 2

SHIP 4

15° S

CRO

30° S

OPEN SYMBOLS — SIGNAL ACQUISITION
CLOSED SYMBOLS — SIGNAL LOSS

LUNAR ORBIT INS.
t=63.28 hr.
h=196,656 n. mi.

CNB

75°E   90°E   105°E   120°E   135°E   150°E   165°E   180°   165°W   150°W   135°W   12

Technician tracks Apollo.

Mars antenna at huge Goldstone site.

Apollo spacecraft during ocean recovery.

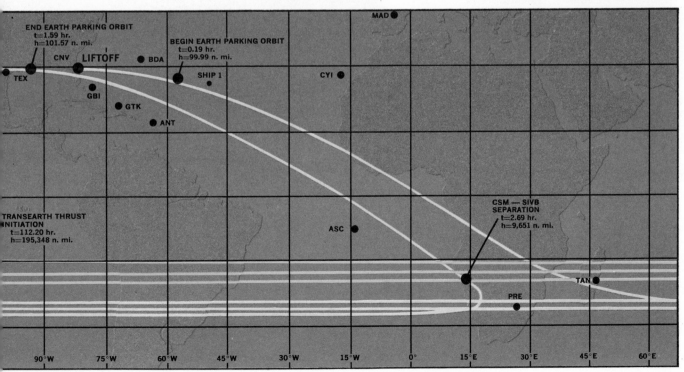

END EARTH PARKING ORBIT
t=1.59 hr.
h=101.57 n. mi.

BEGIN EARTH PARKING ORBIT
t=0.19 hr.
h=99.99 n. mi.

MAD

CNV LIFTOFF   ● BDA

● TEX

● GBI

● GTK

SHIP 1

CYI

● ANT

TRANSEARTH THRUST
INITIATION
t=112.20 hr.
h=195,348 n. mi.

ASC

CSM — SIVB
SEPARATION
t=2.69 hr.
h=9,651 n. mi.

TAN

PRE

90°W   75°W   60°W   45°W   30°W   15°W   0°   15°E   30°E   45°E   60°E

tion with an orbiting or lunar-bound spaceship. The U. S. Army Signal Corps' Project Diana successfully bounced radio signals off the moon and received them back on earth. The way was open to begin planning a space communications network for use at such time as satellites and spacecraft would become actualities.

In 1961, when the late President John F. Kennedy committed the United States to the Apollo program to put a man on the moon and return him to earth in that decade, the National Aeronautics and Space Administration already had in operation the beginnings of a vast sky-track/network of myriad radio frequencies, linking scientific satellites with earth. Worldwide ground stations, computers and other electronics links formed a vast hookup called STADAN (Space Tracking And Data Acquisition Network).

A second global network called NASCOM (NASA Communications Network) soon was established to assist program scientists and mission directors in keeping in touch and coordinating specific missions. Like STADAN, NASCOM operates from NASA's Goddard Space Flight Center at Greenbelt, Maryland, near Washington, D. C., a 100,000 mile network of teletype, voice and digital data links connecting 89 locations in the United States and abroad.

When the first Mercury manned space flights began, NASCOM put into operation a voice communications switchboard system called SCAMA (Station Conferencing And Monitoring Arrangement). And while placing a man in a spaceship added a decision-making human factor, manned space flight still demanded ground support, and for safety reasons, maximum high-speed machine computations for "go, no-go" and other critical decisions. At the Houston Manned Spacecraft Center, giant computers were installed to accept radar and telemetry data in digital form via Goddard, and to perform almost instantly complex computations for launch, orbit and recovery phases of each manned space flight.

As an outgrowth of these early spacecraft communications networks, Goddard next developed the sophisticated Apollo Manned Space Flight Network (MSFN), consisting of 14 ground stations, four instrumented ships and eight instrumented Apollo/Range Instrumentation Aircraft (ARIAs), providing real-time (no delay) data links between the Apollo moonship and the Houston Control Center.

Apollo imposed severe new work loads on MSFN, unlike the earlier Mercury and Gemini flights in which only a single spacecraft was involved. With the moonship, Houston must keep in constant touch simultaneously with the launch vehicle's S-I, S-II and S-IVB stages, with the Command Service Module (CSM) and the Lunar Module (LM), and with the astronauts themselves when they leave their spacecraft to perform extra-vehicular duties or travel away from the LM on lunar surface expeditions.

To Apollo project scientists, the most critical part of the entire moon mission is the lunar field trip during which one astronaut collects rock samples of the moon's crust while a second astronaut records the activities on film. Field trips may run two or three hours, during which the moon explorers are directed to keep up a running monologue, describing by free association whatever interests them. Highly trained in this technique during field trips back on earth, their voices, monitored at Houston via the LM or CM transceiving equipment, supply information for selenologists waiting anxiously to find out what the moon is made of.

On a typical Apollo launch, Cape Kennedy connects directly to Houston via NASCOM's Apollo Launch Data System; after launch, all network and tracking data flows directly to Houston's Manned Spacecraft Center. During orbit flight the tracking responsibility shifts from station to station as the spacecraft circles the earth.

To insure constant contact with the Apollo, three synchronous satellites are used for relay stations. Two of these are Applications Technology Satellites (ATS-1 and ATS-3); the third is Intelsat II. ATS-1 hovering 22,300 miles above the Pacific Ocean provides a voice link between Apollo and Houston via three tracking ships, *Mercury, Huntsville* and *Redstone.* Above the Atlantic, ATS-3 and Intelsat II maintain voice and picture links via tracking ship *Vanguard* and NASA's Canary Island ground station.

Using this relay system, remarkable television coverage of the Apollo 9 splashdown and recovery operations was made from the deck of the aircraft carrier *Guadalcanal,* via ATS-3 to the NASA ground station at Rosman, North Carolina, and thence by land line to New York for commercial broadcast distribution. Intelsat II also provided voice and data information support for Apollo 9, via the Canary Islands station.

Initial full checkout of the Manned Space Flight Network took place during Apollo 4's first orbital mission on November 9, 1967. It also provided a chance to check out fully the most significant electronics system addition to the network for the lunar mission—the Unified S-Band (USB) system which was adopted because it offered a way to stay in touch with three vehicles in earth orbit (Command Module, Lunar Module and S-IVB stage); with the CM and LM throughout the lunar mission; and with the CM during re-entry of the earth's atmosphere.

The USB system combines all functions of acquisition, telemetry, command, voice and tracking on a single radio link, and while this increases the task of data processing, it cuts down the number of required antenna mounts, transmitters, receivers and so on.

The four Apollo Instrumentation Ships (AIS) play a significant role in the overall Apollo mission, particularly during the critical period when the spacecraft must be boosted out of its parking orbit and injected into the lunar trajectory. Since injec

Each astronaut wears a headset with two independently operating earphones and twin microphones with self-contained pre-amplifiers. In front of each man in the spaceship is an audio control panel, enabling him to pre-select what he wants to hear and to whom he wishes to speak. Voice transmission and reception use either the S-Band or VHF/AM systems, and the push-to-talk switch button can also be used as a telegraph key, should the astronaut's voice fail in an emergency.

The spacecraft structure contains sensors to gather data on status and performance of all subsystems in the moonship during flight. Biomedical, TV and timing data also can be processed, stored and transmitted to earth.

The job of handling this vast amount of down-data is assigned to the three prime 85-foot Apollo Network stations at Goldstone, Madrid and Carnarvon as soon as the moonship is about 10,000 miles on its way to the moon, with the other 11 ground stations of the Apollo Network used for backup. Mission Control Center at Houston also sends commands and other up-data back to the spaceship via the same three prime stations during the translunar and lunar phases, over microwave and satellite relay links.

A visit to the Goldstone Apollo station is almost like a visit to the moon, for Goldstone lies inside a desolate natural amphitheater on the Mojave Desert, hostile as the moon itself. Standing like giant mushrooms after a rain are five dish antennas which operate on S-Band frequencies, their power multiplied a thousand times by ruby-crystal masers. Dominating the scene is a 210-foot dish called Mars Station, a metallic ear so sensitive it can monitor spacecraft so far away across the solar system their signal strength may be only one billionth of one billionth watt.

The other four stations, named Echo, Pioneer, Venus and Apollo, are 85-foot dishes. The Apollo Station alone is not a part of NASA's Deep Space Network, which keeps track of interplanetary flights. Sometimes one or more of the deep space dishes may be called upon for backup duties on an Apollo flight, giving the Apollo Manned Spaceflight Network maximum flexibility when messages may be flying back and forth between Houston, the lunar-orbiting Command Module and men on the moon itself.

The feeling exists at Goldstone that the moon is not very far away after all, and that its secrets being unlocked by Apollo astronauts in some way relate to the history of the earth itself.

Not long ago, a Goldstone technician wandered up the hill behind Echo Station and picked up a perfect Indian spearhead, dropped some 10,000 years ago by a pre-Folsom hunter. The find caused as much excitement among the Goldstone scientists as if an Apollo astronaut on the moon had radioed back that he had found evidence of intelligent life on our nearest celestial neighbor.

tion occurs over a broad ocean area between Bermuda and Antigua, a tracking ship must stand by to fill the gap between those island stations. Immediately prior to injection, a complete in-flight countdown is run on the spaceship while still in parking orbit, and here both ships and land stations handle a mass of "down data" coming from Apollo for transfer to Houston Mission Control Center, to decide exactly when to fire the S-IVB booster that kicks the craft on its way to the moon.

Tracking and communication during the translunar and lunar phases of the flight are handled primarily through three 85-foot deep-space dish antennas of the Apollo network, at Goldstone, California; Madrid, Spain; and Carnarvon, Australia. These stations are approximately 120 degrees apart, so that as the earth rotation cuts off one station's direct-line contact with the Apollo ship, the next station rises above the horizon to take over.

To insure that the whole system is working properly, before each Apollo launch the entire communications network makes a dry run, using a special Test and Training Satellite (TTS) looping the earth in a highly elliptical orbit to simulate the flight of a moonship.

Perhaps the most important segment of the entire system is the electronics gear carried aboard the Apollo craft itself. This subsystem falls into four separate categories—intercommunications (voice), data, radio frequency equipment and antennas.

ORBIT OF THE SUN

ORBIT OF MERCURY, 36 MILLION MILES FROM THE SUN

ORBIT OF VENUS, 67 MILLION MILES FROM THE SUN

ORBIT OF EARTH, 93 MILLION MILES FROM THE SUN

ORBIT OF MARS, 141 MILLION MILES FROM THE SUN

ORBIT OF JUPITER, 484 MILLION MILES FROM THE SUN

ORBIT OF SATURN, 887 MILLION MILES FROM THE SUN

ORBIT OF URANUS, 1.787 BILLION MILES FROM THE SUN

ORBIT OF NEPTUNE, 2.797 BILLION MILES FROM THE SUN

ORBIT OF PLUTO, 3.675 BILLION MILES FROM THE SUN

THE SOLAR SYSTEM

BY DR. ELLIS D. MINER

Since the dawn of history man has studied the sky. The sun was the brightest object he saw; its rising and setting determined the length of his day and gave him warmth and light. Many even worshipped the sun.

Ancient man found the moon also interesting to look at. Sometimes it appeared to be a full white disk, while at other times it was only half lighted, and about every 28 days it seemed to disappear altogether.

Possibly the most exciting objects to study were the many thousands of tiny points of light in the dark night sky. These stars all had their own positions in the sky and apparently did not move closer together or farther apart, even though the whole system of stars moved as a group across the night sky in the same way the sun moved across the daytime sky.

In time these ancient astronomers noticed that there were five bright stars which moved slowly among the rest of the stars. These were called planets, meaning "wandering stars". The astronomers gave names to most of the brighter stars. The five bright wandering stars were named Mercury, Venus, Mars, Jupiter and Saturn. The rest of the sky was divided into named areas called constellations, in much the same way that our country is divided into states.

For thousands of years astronomers studied the heavens, but they had only their naked eyes with which to look at these objects in the skies. From these studies they believed the stars were all set on the inside of a huge ball which rotated around the earth. Inside this ball of stars the sun, moon and five planets were thought to revolve around the earth also, but at slightly different speeds than the stars.

Then in 1609 an Italian astronomer named Galileo experimented with some small glass lenses and invented a telescope. With this telescope the moon appeared to be much closer, and one could even see craters and mountains and other markings on the moon which had never before been seen by man. In 1610, Galileo drew the first map of the moon as seen through a telescope. On January 7, 1610, he turned his telescope toward the planet Jupiter, and to his surprise there were four little moons near Jupiter. As he continued to look at the moons during the following nights, he was soon convinced that they were actually circling around the planet Jupiter.

Almost a hundred years earlier a Polish astronomer named Copernicus explained that most all the movements of the stars, the sun, the moon and the planets could be explained if the earth turned on its own axis, and if the earth and the planets all moved around the sun. The moon was still supposed to revolve around the earth. The ideas of Copernicus

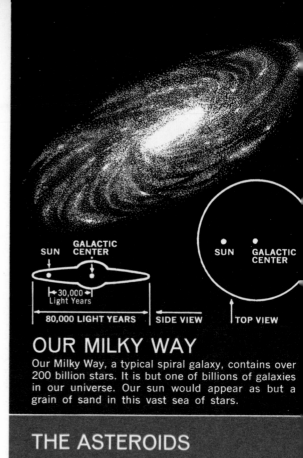

OUR MILKY WAY

Our Milky Way, a typical spiral galaxy, contains over 200 billion stars. It is but one of billions of galaxies in our universe. Our sun would appear as but a grain of sand in this vast sea of stars.

THE ASTEROIDS

Asteroids form a vast belt of irregular rock-like debris orbiting between the inner and outer planet groups. They range in size from dust grain particles to mountain size masses weighing millions of tons. Many asteroids are only a mile or two in diameter, but the largest four, called Ceres, Pallas, Juno, and Vesta, have diameters of 480, 300, 120, and 240 miles. Studies conducted on close approach asteroids have concluded that their capture by spacecraft could have great exploratory, strategic and commercial value.

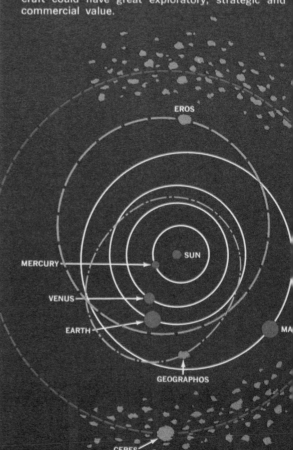

SOME PLANETARY DATA	MERCURY	VENUS	EARTH	MARS	JUPITER	SATURN	URANUS	NEPTUNE	PLUTO
Sidereal period—day/years	88 d	225 d	365.3 d	687 d	11.9 y	29.5 y	84.0 y	164.8 y	248.4 y
Orbital velocity—miles/sec.	29.8	21.8	18.5	15.0	8.1	6.0	4.2	3.4	2.9
Mean diameter—miles	3100	7600	7927	4240	88,700	75,100	29,400	26,800	3560
Length of day	180 d	?	23 h. 56 m.	24 h. 37 m.	9 h. 50 m.	10 h. 14 m.	10 h. 49 m.	14 h. ?	6.4 d ?
Surface temperature Maximum local noon	+660° F.	+800° F.	+140° F.	+50° F.	−216° F.	−243° F.	−300° F.?	−330° F.?	−350° F.?
Minimum midnight	−460° F.?	?	−120° F.	−90° F.	—	—	—	—	—

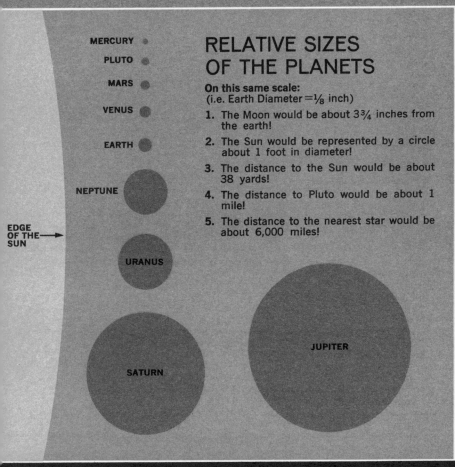

RELATIVE SIZES OF THE PLANETS

On this same scale:
(i.e. Earth Diameter = 1/8 inch)

1. The Moon would be about 3¾ inches from the earth!
2. The Sun would be represented by a circle about 1 foot in diameter!
3. The distance to the Sun would be about 38 yards!
4. The distance to Pluto would be about 1 mile!
5. The distance to the nearest star would be about 6,000 miles!

MERCURY
PLUTO
MARS
VENUS
EARTH
NEPTUNE
URANUS
SATURN
JUPITER

EDGE OF THE SUN →

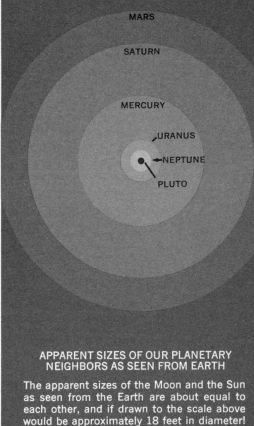

MARS
SATURN
MERCURY
URANUS
←NEPTUNE
PLUTO

APPARENT SIZES OF OUR PLANETARY NEIGHBORS AS SEEN FROM EARTH

The apparent sizes of the Moon and the Sun as seen from the Earth are about equal to each other, and if drawn to the scale above would be approximately 18 feet in diameter!

Comets are the most unusual members of the solar system. A bright comet appears as a hazy star-like object followed by a glowing "tail." A comet itself is a chunk of frozen gas and ice approximately 10 miles or less in diameter. As it approaches the sun, the nucleus material begins to vaporize and a huge glowing cloud begins to grow around the nucleus. The radiation pressure from the sun causes the gas to stream out in a long tail, always pointing away from the sun. The Great Comet of 1843 had the longest tail on record, fully 200 million miles.

THE COMETS

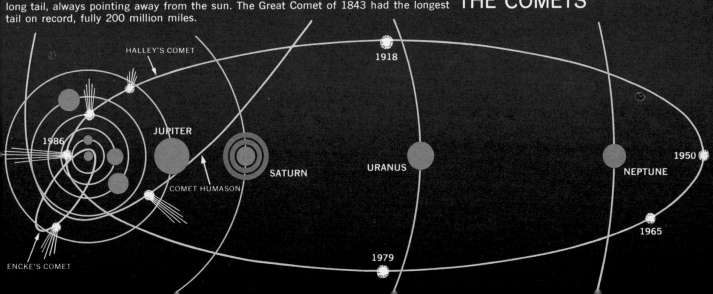

HALLEY'S COMET
1918
1986
JUPITER
COMET HUMASON
SATURN
URANUS
1950
NEPTUNE
1965
1979
ENCKE'S COMET

were so new and different from what most astronomers at that time believed that very few even listened to him. Those who did listen argued that the moon would be left behind if the earth moved around the sun. Then Galileo discovered with his telescope that the moons circling around Jupiter were not left behind as Jupiter moved. If *they* could stay with Jupiter then certainly the moon could stay with the earth.

What is the Solar System? What does it include? What are its limits? For us here on the earth, the biggest and most important object in the sky is our sun. It is a star just like many other stars we see each night. It is neither the hottest nor the coolest, the largest nor the smallest. But it is the closest! The sun is about 93,000,000 miles from the earth. The next closest star is about 25,000,000,000,000 miles away! It takes light, travelling at 186,000 miles a second, 8½ minutes to travel from the sun to the earth. Light now arriving at the earth from the next nearest star started from there about 4½ years ago! Our Solar System includes only one star: the sun. Circling our sun and included in our solar system are 9 planets, at least 32 satellites (moons), and possibly over 100,000 asteroids, or minor planets, ranging in size from a few hundred miles to a few feet or smaller in diameter. An unknown number of comets also circle the sun, becoming visible only when they are within one or two hundred million miles of the sun. At such times they may develop tails which can reach millions of miles in length. Billions of tiny meteors also circle the sun. When one of these meteors enters the atmosphere of the earth, it glows white hot and is commonly known as a "falling star."

How is a planet different from a star? If we come into a completely dark room nothing can be seen. If someone then turns on the light, we are suddenly able to see walls, ceiling, floor and furniture. In our solar system, we may compare the sun to a light in a room that would otherwise be dark. Both the sun and the light bulb glow because they are hot. The same is true of stars we see at night. Our sun has a temperature of about 11,000 degrees at its surface. According to scientists who have made studies of the sun, it may be 35,000,000 degrees near the center!

The planets, on the other hand, are visible only because they reflect the light of the sun, in much the same way that the furniture reflects the light that comes to it from the light bulb. Without the light of the sun the planets would be invisible to us.

How are the planets different from each other? There are nine planets circling the sun. The closest to the sun is Mercury. It is also the smallest, measuring only 2900 miles in diameter. Mercury circles the sun every 88 days. Astronomers thought at one time that Mercury always kept one side

EARTH'S SIZE IN PROPORTION

SOLAR PROMINENCE

These eruptions can reach heights of several hundred thousand miles from the surface of the Sun. This photo which was taken in 1947 shows an altitude of 132,000 miles.

The entire limb of the sun photographed by means of a spectroheliograph in violet light of the calcium K line. Several prominences visible.

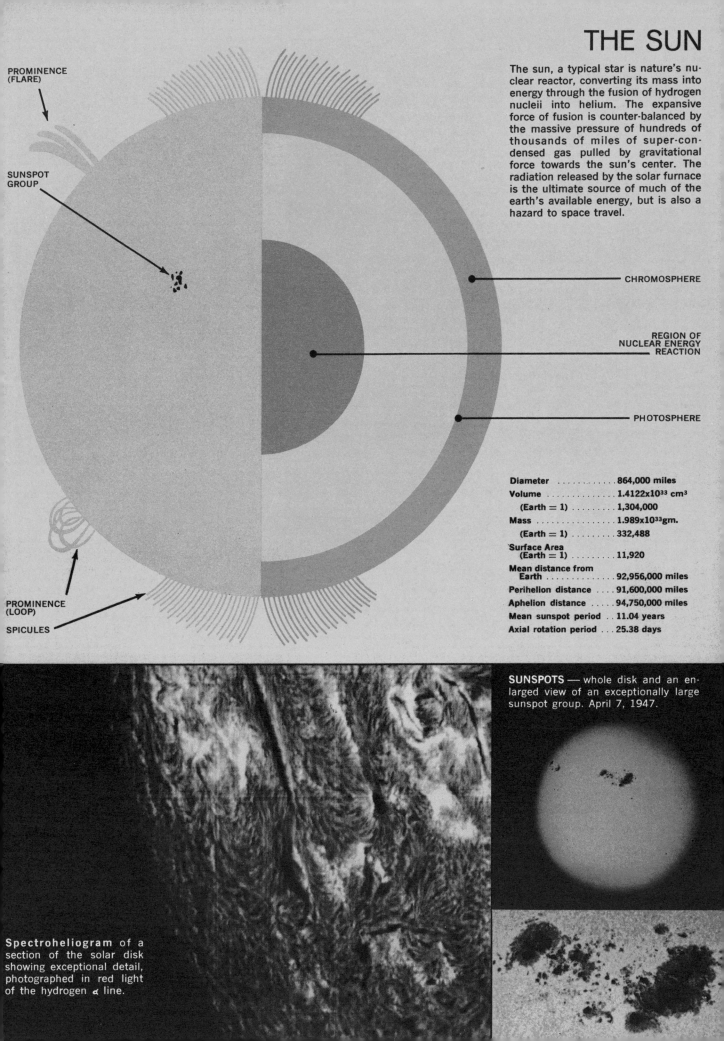

THE SUN

The sun, a typical star is nature's nuclear reactor, converting its mass into energy through the fusion of hydrogen nucleii into helium. The expansive force of fusion is counter-balanced by the massive pressure of hundreds of thousands of miles of super-condensed gas pulled by gravitational force towards the sun's center. The radiation released by the solar furnace is the ultimate source of much of the earth's available energy, but is also a hazard to space travel.

PROMINENCE (FLARE)

SUNSPOT GROUP

PROMINENCE (LOOP)

SPICULES

CHROMOSPHERE

REGION OF NUCLEAR ENERGY REACTION

PHOTOSPHERE

Diameter	864,000 miles
Volume	1.4122×10^{33} cm³
(Earth = 1)	1,304,000
Mass	1.989×10^{33} gm.
(Earth = 1)	332,488
Surface Area (Earth = 1)	11,920
Mean distance from Earth	92,956,000 miles
Perihelion distance	91,600,000 miles
Aphelion distance	94,750,000 miles
Mean sunspot period	11.04 years
Axial rotation period	25.38 days

SUNSPOTS — whole disk and an enlarged view of an exceptionally large sunspot group. April 7, 1947.

Spectroheliogram of a section of the solar disk showing exceptional detail, photographed in red light of the hydrogen α line.

facing the sun, leaving the other side forever in darkness. They have recently discovered, however, that it rotates on its own axis every 59 days, so that an average point on Mercury would have 88 days of darkness followed by 88 days of daylight. During the darkness, the temperature may drop as low as 460 degrees below zero! From the earth we see no sign of an atmosphere on Mercury.

The surface of Venus (second closest planet to the sun) appears to be forever hidden to our view by a thick layer of clouds. It completes one revolution around the sun in 225 days. Even though its surface is invisible, astronomers have succeeded in bouncing radar off the surface of Venus. By studying the radar that returns to earth, they conclude that Venus is rotating very slowly—backwards! That is, on Venus the sun would rise in the west and set in the east. Venus is slightly smaller than the earth. Because it is between us and the sun when it is closest to the earth, Venus' lighted side points away from us and we see only a thin crescent shape.

The third planet from the sun is our own earth. We live on the surface of a planet which has many similarities to other planets in the solar system. It seems to be very different from the other planets in one respect, however: as far as we have been able to tell, earth is the only planet which is suitable as a dwelling place for man

Continuing outward from the sun we next come to Mars with its two small moons, Phobos and Deimos. Phobos, the larger of the two, is probably not more than 10 miles in diameter. Mars is the third smallest planet in the solar system: 4140 miles in diameter. A day on this red planet is about 24½ hours long, but a Martian year is nearly two earth years long. Mars has a very thin atmosphere which allows its surface to be visible most of the time. Polar caps are generally visible as well as many other light and dark markings. Curiously, the colors of these markings sometimes change with the seasons on Mars, leading many scientists to believe that some sort of primitive plant life exists there. Because of this possibility, Mars has probably been studied more than all the other planets put together.

Have you ever heard of the "canals" on Mars? In 1877 an Italian astronomer saw markings on the planet which he called "canali," meaning channels or grooves. But the word was translated into English as "canals." Since we usually think of canals as man-made waterways, arguments were soon started about whether Mars' canals were man-made or not. The most recent findings seem to show that life on Mars would not be possible for man, but we still do not know how to interpret the markings and changes we have seen.

If we skip for the moment the next four planets we come to Pluto, the farthest planet from the sun in our solar system. At a distance of more than 3

VENUS

Venus is about same size as earth, but atmosphere is always cloudy. Clouds are mostly carbon dioxide so man could not breathe the air. Venus is closest of planets to earth.

MERCURY

Mercury is almost 50,000,000 miles from earth at closest point. The atmosphere is very thin, and could not sustain man. During the day, temperature exceeds 700°F.

NEPTUNE

Neptune cannot be seen without a powerful telescope, and then it is very hard to distinguish. It has two moons. Neptune was discovered in mid-1800's.

URANUS

Uranus was discovered by an amateur German astronomer in 1781 with homemade telescopes. Due to unusual axis tilt, days and nights are often 21 years long. This planet has five moons, or satellites.

SATURN

Saturn is the most outstanding planet to see, with its ring of small matter. Like some other planets, it is much less dense than the earth and is covered by a dense gas.

upiter is a giant planet and is three times farther from the sun than Mars. One year of Jupiter is nearly twelve times longer than ours, but each day s only ten hours long. This planet is covered by a dense layer of gas.

JUPITER

Mars is most interesting to astronomers, because there might be plant life on it. There is little chance man could live there, as the atmosphere is thin. Mars has two moons.

MARS

PLUTO

Pluto was discovered in 1930, and is smaller than the earth. It marks the boundary of our solar system, and has a day equal to about six of ours.

billion miles, the sun looks only like a bright star in the sky and sheds very little light on Pluto. It takes Pluto 248 years to circle the sun a single time! Its day is probably about 6½ earth days in length. Pluto is perhaps just a little smaller than Mars, making it the second smallest planet. Because of its great distance, very little more is known about it.

The highs and lows of temperature are very great on Mercury, Venus, Mars, and Pluto. Very little water exists on these planets. Their atmospheres are not made of the gases man or plants need to breathe. Therefore, except possibly for Mars, we feel certain that life as we know it would not survive on these planets. But what about the other planets in our solar system? Is it possible that they could support life?

The four largest planets are Jupiter, Saturn, Uranus, and Neptune. That is their order in distance from the sun and also in size. Jupiter is the giant of our solar system, bigger than all the other planets combined. It has the most moons as well: 12 in all. It has a diameter more than ten times as large as the earth. In spite of its great size its day is less than 10 hours long, and this rapid spinning causes Jupiter to be flattened at its poles and bulge at its middle. Saturn, which has a day just over 10 hours long, has an even more squashed look. In addition, Saturn has a huge ring system circling its equator. The ring is composed of millions of particles, each gliding around Saturn in much the same way that each of Saturn's 10 moons do.

Uranus and Neptune are very nearly twins because of their similar size and greenish color. Uranus has a diameter of about 29,400 miles, Neptune of about 28,000. Uranus has five known moons, Neptune has two.

All of the four largest planets have extremely low temperatures and atmospheres that are poisonous to man and most other forms of life we know. Our exploration of all the planets will continue, but we are not likely to find any other place within our solar system where we could live without protective space suits. Why, then, are we so anxious to continue to explore the solar system?

The simplest answer is that we are curious. There is so much we don't know about the other planets that we would like to know. Our own atmosphere makes things difficult for us. Much of the light from the planets never reaches us because our atmosphere stops it. The light that does reach us is generally blurred by motion of the air between us and the planets.

But of what value will this added knowledge be to us here on earth? The answer to this question is also simple, for the more we learn about the other planets, the more we understand about earth.

Dr. Miner is an Astronomer at Jet Propulsion Laboratory, Space Sciences Division, California Institute of Technology.

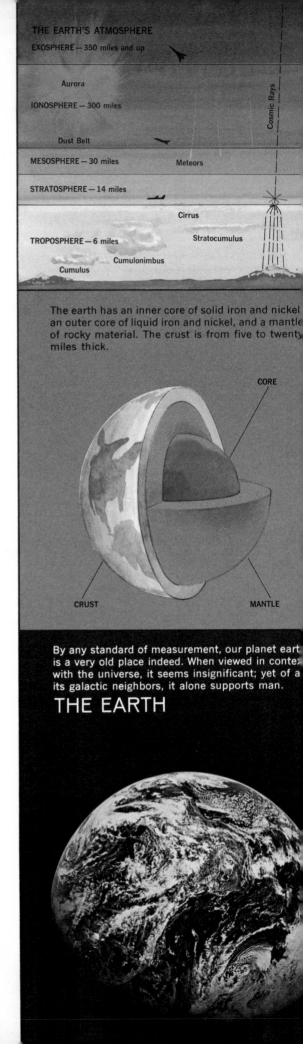

THE EARTH'S ATMOSPHERE
EXOSPHERE — 350 miles and up

Aurora

IONOSPHERE — 300 miles

Dust Belt

MESOSPHERE — 30 miles   Meteors

STRATOSPHERE — 14 miles

Cirrus

Stratocumulus

TROPOSPHERE — 6 miles

Cumulonimbus

Cumulus

Cosmic Rays

The earth has an inner core of solid iron and nickel an outer core of liquid iron and nickel, and a mantle of rocky material. The crust is from five to twenty miles thick.

CORE

CRUST   MANTLE

By any standard of measurement, our planet earth is a very old place indeed. When viewed in contex with the universe, it seems insignificant; yet of a its galactic neighbors, it alone supports man.

THE EARTH

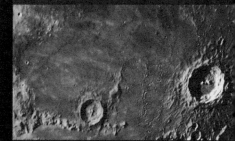

Region of Ptolemy and Tycho.

Region of Crater Copernicus.

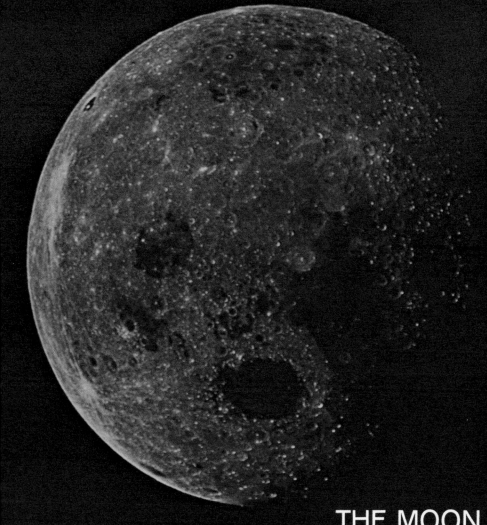

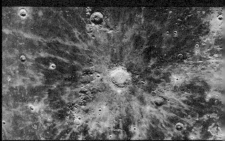

Crater Clavius.

Crater Copernicus.

THE MOON

The Moon is one of the very few places within the Solar System where the events of cosmic time are recorded. The Moon is a quiet world where the events of its lifetime remain silently etched upon its surface. Manned expeditions to the Moon will be but a stepping stone to even greater space adventures. This first journey could well determine not only the destiny of man's achievement in space but also his future on earth.

PHASES OF THE MOON

As the moon orbits around the earth, the sun's rays reflect on one side. When the moon is nearest to the sun, we would see only its dark side. When it is farthest from the sun, we then see its full lighted surface.

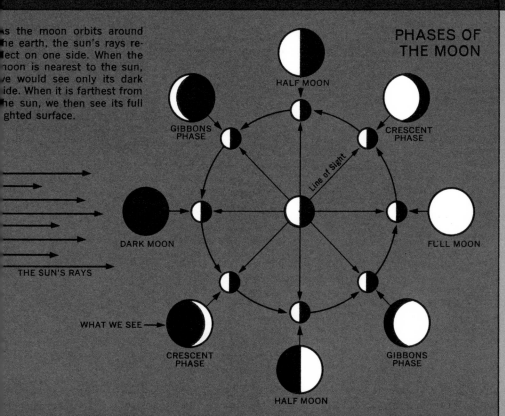

HALF MOON

GIBBONS PHASE

CRESCENT PHASE

Line of Sight

THE SUN'S RAYS

DARK MOON

FULL MOON

WHAT WE SEE

CRESCENT PHASE

GIBBONS PHASE

HALF MOON

GENERAL MOON DATA

Mean Diameter	2160 miles
Escape Velocity (Full Moon)	1.37 miles/sec
Escape Velocity (New Moon)	1.52 miles/sec
Orbital eccentricity (1900.0)	0.05900489
Mean Distance from Earth	238,857 miles
Sidereal Month (1900.0), true period of revolution	27.3216610 days
Earth to Lunar Mass Ratio	81.366
Mean Orbital Speed (1900.0)	3370.3 ft/sec
Temperature variation	100 to 389°K or —279 to +243°F
Craters: total number visible	> 300,000
Highest Mountains: Leibnitz Mountains	29,000 feet
Doerfel Mountains	18,325 feet

YOUR FUTURE IN SPACE

BY JAMES R. ASWELL

ILLUSTRATIONS BY JOHN BROOKS MILLER

You can have an exciting and rewarding career in your country's program to explore and use space. When you finish college, many thousands of qualified young men and women will be needed. By that time, the United States should have a large space station circling in orbit far above the earth. As many as a hundred people may be living in the station, carrying out scientific work. At the same time, the United States will probably have built a scientific station on the moon. Astronauts will be making long trips on the moon's surface to learn about everything there.

Even more exciting, it is likely that astronauts in much larger spaceships than we have at present will be training to go millions of miles from earth to Mars and Venus. Plans will be under way to reach even more distant planets in our solar system.

Today there are some 50 trained astronauts. Ten years from now there should be hundreds. Many thousands more qualified people than now will be working to launch the giant rockets that send spacecraft on voyages. Others will be designing and building the rockets and spaceships. Still others will be studying and finding out how to use the great amounts of new knowledge that spacecraft will be radioing back to earth.

Qualified is the word to remember when you plan to seek a Space Age career. It means that you should start studying hard now. You should determine to make high marks in college. Boys and girls who barely get by in their school work will have little chance to find important jobs in the space program.

Years ago a high school boy in Germany was doing poorly in his studies. He was far more interested in his hobby than in school work. Rockets were his hobby. He spent most of his time building small, crude rockets and shooting them off in the fields. He neglected his school homework. He was convinced that the world would enter a space age within his lifetime. He believed that men would be rocketed to the moon and the planets; his fondest dream was to take a leading part in the coming Space Age.

A teacher who knew about the boy's ambition took him aside and said something like this:

"When you are a grown man, you want to design big rockets. But you are failing in mathematics. The big rockets you dream of will be complicated. The men who build them will have to be experts in mathematics. So if you want to design and build such rockets, you will have to turn over a new leaf. You will have to catch up on mathematics and your other subjects. You will have to master them. Otherwise, if a space age does come, you will surely find yourself standing on the sidelines, envying those who worked hard to qualify for space. Think it over."

The boy took to heart what the teacher had said. He did not drop his hobby of rocketry but he did not let it take up the time he needed to spend on his studies. He became a fine mathematician. He did well in his other studies in high school and college. And when the time came to design powerful rockets, he was well *qualified.*

The German boy was Wernher von Braun. After World War II, he came to the United States where our government placed him in charge of building big military rockets. Then, in 1958, he was transferred to the new civilian space agency, the National Aeronautics and Space Administration—better known as NASA. Dr. von Braun and a team of NASA experts designed and developed the Saturn rocket for the Project Apollo moon program.

On television you have seen the launching of the giant Saturn which has boosted astronauts into earth orbits and sent them 240,000 miles to the moon. Saturn burns enough fuel to fill 150 railroad tank cars. It produces more power as it sends astronauts into space than 200,000 medium-sized automobiles. And Saturn has 5 million working parts. Think of it—5 million parts and every last one of them must work perfectly!

Many people mistakenly think that only men hold important positions in the space program. Actually, NASA now has more than 260 women working in high-level jobs on an equal footing with men. For example, a gifted woman is head of the entire NASA astronomy program. Another woman tells the astronauts what they should observe and report during their flights in space. Other women are doing important work in many fields, ranging from mathematics, chemistry, and medicine to key jobs in helping manage the space effort. As the space program goes on, it will offer more and more career opportunities to qualified women.

You may be able to qualify as an astronaut if, among other things, you graduate from college with high marks and a degree in engineering or science. All astronauts must be citizens of the United States. They must be no taller than six feet because quarters in spacecraft are cramped. They must be no older than 34 years of age. Those who will pilot spaceships must have at least 1,000 hours of experience as jet pilots or must have had similar experience with the Armed Forces, NASA, or the aircraft industry.

Another group of astronauts need not be jet pilots before they are accepted for training. They are scientist-astronauts. Each is required to have a degree in one of the branches of science related to space. These astronauts must meet the same qualifications of citizenship, age, and size as pilot-astronauts. The scientist-astronauts are given training in piloting aircraft and spacecraft.

So far, no woman who has applied to become an astronaut has been able to fulfill all the qualifications. In the future, however, there may be many woman astronauts. The Russians have already sent a young woman cosmonaut in orbit around the earth.

In addition to astronauts, four kinds of experts are in great demand and will continue to be in demand during coming years. They are: scientists, engineers, technicians, and managers.

Scientists investigate the laws of nature and the universe to find out how they operate. They analyze what space is like. They learn about the sun, the moon, the planets in our solar system, and the stars billions of miles distant. Their work is called "basic research."

Engineers design all types of space instruments and equipment. This includes rockets and spacecraft. Engineers build on the basic knowledge discovered and explained by the scientists, with whom they work closely. Their work is called "applied research" because they make practical use of scientific knowledge to solve problems on earth and in space.

Technicians are highly trained assistants to scientists and engineers. They are skilled workmen who build and often operate a wide variety of space equipment such as radar, radio, computers, and the like. Some technicians have college degrees. Women technicians serve in NASA research programs of many kinds. A number of them are nurses who look after the health of the astronauts.

Managers are the businessmen of the space program. They are in charge of spending billions of dollars a year. They administer the work of NASA headquarters in Washington and of the hundreds of research and development projects going forward in 10 NASA centers in different parts of the country. They also oversee the work of several thousand large and small industrial firms and colleges and other private laboratories which have contracts with NASA to carry out space work.

Before astronauts could go into space and to the moon, scientists had to study and learn about conditions there. They worked with engineers and technicians to build robot spacecraft that were launched to investigate and automatically radio and televise to earth what they found out there.

Some of the craft, making studies of airless space, reported that little or no danger exists of meteors striking manned spaceships. Other unmanned spacecraft were sent to the moon. Taking thousands of television pictures of the surface, they transmitted them back to earth. The pictures were hundreds of times clearer and more detailed than the photographs of the moon taken through the most powerful earth telescopes. Still other robot spacecraft landed on the moon and tested the surface dust and rocks. They found that the surface is strong enough to bear the weight of a small spacecraft carrying astronaut explorers.

The main Apollo spacecraft was designed and constructed by engineers and technicians with the advice of NASA scientists. It carries all the air the astronauts breathe. It is a marvel of special electronics and materials. Apollo has two million functioning parts, most of them electrical. Although the main spacecraft is only large enough to carry three men, it is packed with equipment connected by 15 miles of wiring. Some of the electronic parts are so tiny that they can be seen only with the aid of a microscope.

Materials engineers devised an amazing heat shield

for Apollo. When the spacecraft returns from the moon and hits the earth's atmosphere at a speed of 25,000 miles per hour, terrific air friction builds up. If the craft were built of ordinary metal, it would burn like a fireball or a shooting star. Fortunately the Apollo heat shield can withstand a temperature half as hot as the surface of the sun! The astronauts never feel the fiery heat outside. Fully protected, they remain in perfect comfort in their Apollo cabin.

Ten years from now the space program will employ many more technicians than today. For example, there may be hundreds of specialized unmanned satellites orbiting the earth. Much improved weather satellites will be making long-range weather predictions possible. There will be more communication satellites than now. They will make it possible to send and receive television, telephone calls, and other electronic messages from and to any spot on the globe. These and other types of satellite services will create a constantly growing demand for technically trained people.

Technicians will build service satellites, track them by radar, switch their equipment on and off by radio, and operate ground receivers, transmitters, and various controls. Some day technicians may even fly out into space to repair satellites if they break down or operate improperly.

The space effort of the future will also employ increasing numbers of secretaries, typists, and clerks. Skilled laborers will be needed to construct launching pads, radar and radio sites, laboratories, and other types of buildings for space centers on earth. There will be a constant need for truck drivers, bulldozer operators, and other workers to carry out hundreds of jobs supporting the space effort. Some space authorities predict that the government and industry program will eventually grow larger than the automobile industry.

Professional salaries in both government space centers and in the space industry are good, and getting better. The trend is toward higher salaries all down the line. Today salaries for scientific and technical specialists start at more than $6,000 a year and go up to as much as $28,000. Astronauts draw from about $10,000 a year to $28,000.

The salaries of managers range from about $8,500 per year to $28,000. For some management positions in space industry, salaries are even higher. Wages for clerical workers and laborers of various types are usually those prevailing in the parts of the country where they work.

If you plan to have a career in the Space Age, you will want to keep up with what is happening and with what experts foresee will be happening when you graduate from college or from a technical training school. You can do this in several ways.

Obviously you will watch launchings and other space activities on television. You should also read what the newspapers and newsmagazines report about the program. In addition, you should read some of the books about space that you will find

either in your school library or the public library. Hundreds of them have been published at the readership levels of young people like you.

Another good way to keep up with what is happening and is planned in the space program is to ask your science teacher to write to NASA requesting that your class be put on the free distribution list to receive NASA FACTS. This publication is especially written for students in junior high and senior high schools. It is illustrated and makes fascinating reading.

Teacher may write for NASA FACTS to:

The Office of Educational Programs
National Aeronautics and Space Administration
Washington, D. C. 20546

The NASA Office of Educational Programs also publishes a detailed GUIDE TO CAREERS IN AEROSPACE TECHNOLOGY which will be mailed to you, free, upon request.

Robert H. Goddard, American rocket pioneer.

A BRIE

One can imagine that ancient man watched the birds and dreamed of flying high in the sky. He could not imagine the great distances to the moon, planets and stars. In fact, he thought of these lights in the sky as gods who were sometimes happy and sometimes angry. When they were happy the sun shone or gentle rain fell on the earth replenishing his water supply. When the gods were angry there were violent storms, lightning and thunder, floods or drought.

Wise men studied the regular movement of the stars. The changing seasons were noted as were the monthly changing of the "shape" of the moon. Life was short and it was difficult to survive even at best efforts. Still, it was pleasurable to dream of flying high, even visiting the silvery moon . . . . . .

2nd Century A.D.

Ptolemy of Alexandria developed the concept of the motion of the sun and planets around the earth, at the center. In 160 A.D. Lucian of Samosota, a Greek, wrote a story of flight to the moon on artificial wings. It would be many centuries before it was discovered that the earth's atmosphere did not extend 1/10,000 the distance to the moon.

10th to 12th Century

Gunpowder—a mixture of sulfur, charcoal and potash—was formulated. When this mixture was set afire it burned rapidly, giving off light, heat and clouds of smoke. As the purity of the ingredients of gunpowder were improved and the formulas standardized this fast-burning mixture was recognized as a source of power. By confining the burning gases in a tube, gunpowder could shoot an iron ball very fast and straight. It was dangerous; a weapon for defense, war and hunting.

13th Century

Someone, probably several persons, discovered that a tube filled with gunpowder and lit at one end gave thrust or a "push" as the gases rushed out. Attaching these tubes of gunpowder to arrows and spears made them travel farther. Soon it was learned that an arrow could fly by itself when enough gunpowder was used. Rocket propulsion had been discovered. "Arrows of flying fire" in China and elsewhere in Europe were reported.

16th Century

Nicholas Copernicus, Polish-German, a mathematician-astronomer established the exact motions of the planets in orbit about the sun.

17th Century

Galileo in 1610, by using the sailor's telescope on the heavens, was the first to use this tool for astronomy. Within a few weeks he had mapped the craters and mountains of the moon. Later he discovered four moons of Jupiter—tiny specks—circling the planet. He judged that they were small because of the distance from the earth. For the first time a scale of distance of proper order of magnitude was realized.

Johannes Kepler correctly established the elliptical, rather than circular, orbits of the planets.

Later in this century Isaac Newton formulated his "laws of motion." Laws of astronomy and physics were now on a firm foundation.

ILLUSTRATIONS BY ROBERT SCHAAR

HISTORY OF SPACE EXPLORATION

BY FREDERICK C. DURANT, III, Assistant Director—Astronautics, Smithsonian Institution

Konstantin E. Tsiolkovsky.

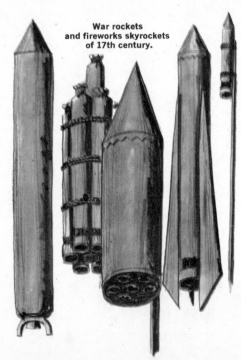

Gerhard Zucker with German mail rocket of 1930's.

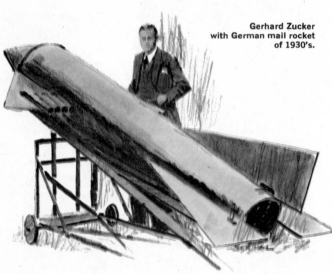

War rockets and fireworks skyrockets of 17th century.

18th Century

In India the British were defeated in battles in which the Indians used hundreds, even thousands, of war rockets. Instead of the paper or cloth rocket tubes they were made of iron, tightly filled with gunpowder and tied to bamboo sticks with strips of hide.

The French Montgolfier brothers flew in a hot air balloon in Paris (1783). Hydrogen balloon flights soon followed. Rockets were widely used in aerial fireworks at celebrations and festivals in London, Paris and Rome.

19th Century

British William Congreve improved and standardized the rocket as a war weapon. He developed explosive and incendiary warheads. Used in sea attacks on the French coast at Boulogne in 1805 and 1806, later at Copenhagen, rockets were also used against the American forces in the War of 1812. The "rockets' red glare," which Francis Scott Key wrote of in our national anthem were Congreve rockets fired from British warships at Ft. McHenry in Baltimore harbor. Every major nation in Europe built rocket weapons and used them in warfare until the rifled barrel artillery became more accurate and replaced them as weapons.

Jules Verne published his great book, *From the Earth to the Moon and A Flight Round it.* This imaginative and exciting story of flight of three men travelling in a spacecraft in a circumlunar flight was immensely popular. It attracted interest in the possibility of space flight. But technology had not developed to the point where the design and construction of a space vehicle was possible. Verne based his story on the building of an immense cannon. A flight based on a cannon would not have been possible.

Other uses were made of rocket power for peaceful purposes. Many lives were saved on sea coasts by using line-carrying rockets to rescue sailors and passengers from ships driven onto rocks by storms. Whaling rockets were developed to hunt these important sources of lamp-oil.

In Russia, a little-known teacher of mathematics, K. E. Tsiolkovski, derived fundamental principles of space flight. He suggested the use of rockets using liquid propellants to achieve much greater thrust than gunpowder.

1900

H. G. Wells published *The First Men on the Moon,* a tale of true science fiction.

1903

The Wright brothers flew in an airplane at Kitty Hawk, North Carolina. It was a short flight—only 120 feet the first time, but it was historic. Man's dream of controlled flight was coming true.

This same year K. E. Tsiolkovski published a detailed book, in Russian, on interplanetary flight using rocket power.

1914

While the clouds of World War I gathered, Robert H. Goddard, a physicist and professor at Clark College, Worcester, Mass. obtained two U. S. patents on rockets. These patents covered the stage-rocket principle, solid and liquid propellants, and basic parts of a rocket motor.

1916

Dr. Robert H. Goddard applied to the Smithsonian Institution in Washington, D. C., for financial support in experiments in rocket power. His interest was to explore this technique to carry scientific instruments to altitudes higher than could be reached by balloons. The Smithsonian responded with an initial grant of $5000 and thus commenced a period of financial support and encouragement that lasted until 1929. (See below.)

1919

A Method of Reaching Extreme Altitudes by Robert H. Goddard was published by the Smithsonian Institution. In this slim report Goddard set forth the basic principles of physics and mathematics of stage-rocket propulsion and described his experiments with rocket motors using smokeless powder. He also suggested that a half-pound of flash powder could be seen by telescopes if shot to the shadowed side of the moon by a rocket.

1923

Hermann Oberth published in Germany, *The Rocket Into Planetary Space.* Oberth, of Transylvania, later a German citizen, was a teacher, as were Tsiolkovski and Goddard. He became the leader of interest in rocket development in Germany.

1926

Robert H. Goddard launched the first liquid propellant rocket at Auburn, Massachusetts on March 16. Although it travelled only 120 ft. it was an historic flight.

1927

Willy Ley, Rudolf Nebel and others formed the German Rocket Society. Soon the members were experimenting with liquid oxygen and gasoline rocket motors. Wernher von Braun, in his teens, became an enthusiastic member.

1929

The Guggenheim family, upon recommendation of Col. Charles Lindbergh, increased support of Robert H. Goddard. Goddard moved his research to Roswell, New Mexico.

1930

In New York, N. Y. the American Interplanetary Society was formed by Edward G. Pendray and others. Later renamed the American Rocket Society, and then the American Institute of Aeronautics and Astronautics, this organization grew to be the largest professional society of its sort in the world.

1931

The German Rocket Society developed a liquid propellant rocket engine producing 110 lb. thrust.

1932

Fredrich Tsander and members of a group in the U.S.S.R. developed a 110 lb. thrust rocket motor.

1934

The German Rocket Society was disbanded. The German Army proceeded to take over rocket development. von Braun, working for the army, developed the A-3 rocket with 660 lb. thrust.

1935

Robert H. Goddard launched a gyro-stabilized rocket at Roswell, N. M. which reached 7500 ft. altitude.

1942-1943

British forces used anti-aircraft rockets against German warplanes and bombardment rockets in infantry engagements. The U.S.S.R. used artillery rockets, known as Katyusha. The U. S. used heavy salvos of rocket fire preceding amphibious landings in the Mediterranean and later in the Pacific campaigns. Aircraft firing rockets were used against tanks and shipping. The shoulder-fired Bazooka rocket was a successful U. S. anti-tank weapon.

In Germany the first A-4, popularly known as the V-2, was successfully tested by von Braun as technical director at the Peenemünde research station on the Baltic Sea. A tremendous engineering achievement, the A-4 had a 55,000 lb. thrust, turbopump propellant system rocket engine. Propellants were liquid oxygen and alcohol. Launched first against Paris, thousands were fired at London. Curving down from a ballistic trajectory at a distance of a hundred miles or more, the 1-ton warhead of high explosive struck the ground at supersonic speed, without audible warning.

There were a dozen or more rocket powered guided missiles developed by the German Army and Air Force. A rocket-powered interceptor aircraft, the Mel63 had immense capability in attacking bomber formations. No other nation had developed these technologies to such a degree.

1945

The U. S. Army fired a WAC Corporal research rocket to an altitude of 43.5 miles.

1947

The first of a series of captured German A-4 (V-2) rockets, converted to research vehicles, was fired at White Sands Proving Ground, New Mexico. von Braun and about 100 of his top engineers and

Testing
life-saving rocket
in England
during 1920's.

scientists had surrendered to the U. S. Army in 1945 and had been brought to the United States to work on ballistic missile development.

1949

The first of a series of Navy Viking upper atmosphere research rockets was fired at White Sands. A two-stage V-2 with solid propellant second stage reached an altitude of 244 miles.

1952

First of a series of articles in *Collier's* Magazine by Wernher von Braun appeared. von Braun proposed and argued for a program of space exploration, first with instrumented satellites and then man to the moon and Mars.

1955

President Eisenhower announced that the U. S. would launch an artificial satellite in connection with the International Geophysical Year (IGY). The IGY was a cooperative scientific program of many nations wherein simultaneous geophysical and atmospheric measurements would be made around the world.

1957

Sputnik I was launched by the U.S.S.R. on October 4 as part of the IGY program. Unexpected, this event launched the "space age," This 23 lb.

spacecraft measured air density, temperature, cosmic ray and meteoroid data.

On November 3, the Soviets launched Sputnik II, an 1120 lb. spacecraft carrying a dog, Laika. Biomedical data was obtained on the animal to study the effects of prolonged weightlessness.

1958

On January 31 the first U. S. satellite, Explorer I, was launched at Cape Canaveral, Florida by von Braun and his team, now located at Huntsville, Alabama. The launch vehicle was a modified Redstone ballistic missile with three solid propellant upper stages. An Army program in cooperation with the California Institute of Technology's Jet Propulsion Laboratory, the Explorer I gave indication of the Van Allen Radiation Belt. Explorer III launched a few months later carried a tape recorder which proved the existence of these radiation belts.

On March 1 the first Vanguard satellite was launched at Cape Canaveral by the Naval Research Laboratory. The Soviet Union startled the world on May 15 by launching Sputnik III, a 2925 lb. spacecraft carrying many geophysical experiments.

On December 18 Project Score was launched by the U. S. Air Force. An Atlas launch vehicle was placed in earth orbit carrying a taped Christmas message from President Eisenhower. This was the first voice transmission from space.

Creation of NASA

During 1950, Congressional hearings were held to decide how best to organize the country's technical and scientific resources, industry and government facilities to plan and conduct operations in space. In July 1958 the National Aeronautics and Space Administration (NASA) was created. NASA inherited the former National Advisory Committee for Aeronautics with its facilities at Langley, Virginia, Cleveland, Ohio and Ames, California.

Commencing operations in October, 1958, NASA created Project Mercury in November. The aims of Project Mercury were to put manned spacecraft into a controlled orbit, investigate the capability of man in space and to develop recovery of the spacecraft from orbit. Seven astronauts were selected in April 1959 after a nationwide call for jet, test pilot volunteers.

The one-man Mercury spacecraft was shaped something like a bell, 6½ ft. wide at the bottom and about 9 ft. tall, weighing over 3000 lbs.

Following developmental tests two astronauts, Alan B. Shepard and Virgil "Gus" Grissom, flew ballistic flights in 1961. In these flights a Redstone missile booster hurled the spacecraft to a height of over one hundred miles above the Atlantic Ocean from Cape Canaveral, Florida. On February 1962, astronaut John H. Glenn, Jr. made three orbits of the earth. The orbital booster was a modified Atlas ICBM. Glenn was followed in further orbital flights

Wernher von Braun.

by astronauts M. Scott Carpenter and Walter M. Schirra in 1962 and L. Gordon Cooper in 1963.

Meanwhile the U.S.S.R. had continued to make headlines by impacting Lunik II on the moon, sending Lunik III around the moon, photographing the far side, perpetually hidden from the earth. The photographs were radioed to earth. On April 12, 1961 Soviet Yuri Gagarin became the first man to orbit the earth; one revolution. Four months later Gherman Titov orbited the Earth 17 times.

By now, there were two follow-on U. S. manned programs: Project Apollo to land a man on the moon in this decade, and Project Gemini to develop the technologies required for this accomplishment.

Both Projects Apollo and Gemini ran concurrently. The initial challenge of Apollo was to develop the Saturn class of large launch vehicles. This task was given to Wernher von Braun, now head of the NASA Marshall Space Flight Center at Huntsville, Alabama.

Project Gemini's prime missions were to maneuver in space, rendezvous with a target vehicle and to hard dock with the target. Gemini spacecraft carried two astronauts. Ten Gemini flights totaling 975 hours were flown. Orbital rendezvous was accomplished ten times, docking: nine times. Extra-vehicular activity (EVA) or "walk in space" was effected several times totaling over twelve hours of EVA.

The U.S.S.R., in August 1962, orbited two manned Vostok spacecraft a day apart, effecting a visual rendezvous. In June 1963, two days apart, two more Vostoks were launched. This time one was piloted by a female cosmonaut, Valentina Tereshkova, the first woman to reach space. In October 1964 the Voskhod spacecraft orbited three cosmonauts. In March 1965 Cosmonauts Belayev and Leonov orbited in a Voskhod. During this flight Leonov passed through an airlock and made the first EVA in space.

Up to this point the U.S.S.R. had performed most of the significant "firsts" in space ahead of the United States. This was true not only of the manned but also lunar probe missions. However, the U. S. had apparently made a much greater capital investment in ground support facilities and commitments of funds to a wider variety of programs. Thus by 1968 the Apollo program successes appeared to give the U. S. a distinct lead in manned lunar programs. In Applications satellites—communications, meteorological (weather) and navigation—the level of technology generally, but not always, appeared to be more advanced than in the Soviet Union.

Note: The above chronology has been necessarily brief. For more information see encyclopedias and ask a librarian about related books.

WHERE TO ASK FOR NASA SERVICES FOR THE PUBLIC

If you live in:	**Write to:***
Alaska, Idaho, Montana, Nothern California, Oregon, Washington, Wyoming	NASA Ames Research Center Moffett Field, California 94035
Connecticut, Maine, Massachusetts, New Hampshire, New York, Rhode Island, Vermont	NASA Electronics Research Center 575 Technology Square Cambridge, Massachusetts 02139
Alabama, Arkansas, Louisiana, Mississippi, Missouri, Tennessee	NASA George C. Marshall Space Flight Center Huntsville, Alabama 35812
Delaware, District of Columbia, Maryland, New Jersey, Pennsylvania, West Virginia	NASA Goddard Space Flight Center Greenbelt, Maryland 20771
Florida, Georgia, Puerto Rico, Virgin Islands	NASA John F. Kennedy Space Center Kennedy Space Center, Florida 32899
Kentucky, North Carolina, South Carolina, Virginia	NASA Langley Research Center Langley Station Hampton, Virginia 23365
Illinois, Indiana, Iowa, Michigan, Minnesota, Ohio, Wisconsin	NASA Lewis Research Center 21000 Brookpark Road Cleveland, Ohio 44135
Colorado, Kansas, Nebraska, New Mexico, North Dakota, Oklahoma, South Dakota, Texas	NASA Manned Spacecraft Center Houston, Texas 77058
Arizona, Hawaii, Nevada, Southern California, Utah	NASA Western Support Office 150 Pico Boulevard Santa Monica, California 90406

*When writing, please start the address with the topic in which you are interested, such as:

Teacher Education | Motion Pictures
Education Conferences | TV-Radio
Instructional Resources | Speakers
Publications | Exhibits
Spacemobiles | Tours

FOR FURTHER READING

Reaching for the Stars (Biography of W. von Braun), Bergaust, Erik. New York: Doubleday, 1960.

Man and Space (editors of Life) and Clarke, Arthur C. New York: Life Science Library, Time, Inc., 1965.

The Promise of Space, Clarke, Arthur C. Harper & Row, 1968.

Profiles of the Future, Clarke, Arthur C. New York: Harper & Row, 1963.

Exploring Space With a Camera, Cortright, Edgar M. NASA SP-168, Supt. of Documents, U.S. Govt. Printing Office, Washington, D.C. 20402, 1968

A History of Space Flight, Emme, Eugene M. New York: Holt, Rinehart and Winston, 1965.

This High Man (Biography of Robert H. Goddard), Lehman, Milton. New York: Farrar Strauss, 1963.

Rockets, Missiles and Men in Space, Ley, Willy. New York: Viking, 1968.

Man's Conquest of Space, Shelton, William R. National Geographic Society, Washington, D.C. 20036.

This New Ocean, Swenson, L. S., Grimwood, J. M., Alexander, C. C. A History of Project Mercury. U.S. Government Printing Office, Washington, D.C. 20402, 1966.

History of Rocketry and Space Travel, von Braun, W. and Ordway, F. I. New York: Crowell, 1967.

Space Frontier, von Braun, W. New York: Holt, Rinehart and Winston, 1967.

WHO MAKES THE MOONSHIP?

Contractor	**Item**
Bellcomm Washington, D.C.	Apollo Systems Engineering
The Boeing Co. Washington, D.C.	Technical Integration and Evaluation
General Electric-Apollo Support Dept., Daytona Beach, Fla.	Apollo Checkout and Reliability
North American Rockwell Corp. Space Div., Downey, Calif.	Spacecraft Command and Service Modules
Grumman Aircraft Engineering Corp., Bethpage, N.Y.	Lunar Module
Massachusetts Institute of Technology, Cambridge, Mass.	Guidance & Navigation (Technical Management)
General Motors Corp., AC Electronics Div., Milwaukee	Guidance & Navigation (Manufacturing)
TRW Systems Inc. Redondo Beach, Calif.	Trajectory Analysis
Avco Corp., Space Systems Div., Lowell, Mass.	Heat Shield Ablative Material
North American Rockwell Corp. Rocketdyne Div. Canoga Park, Calif.	J-2 Engines, F-1 Engines
The Boeing Co. New Orleans	First Stages (SIC) of Saturn V Flight Vehicles, Saturn V Systems Engineering and Integration Ground Support Equipment
North American Rockwell Corp. Space Div., Seal Beach, Calif.	Development and Production of Saturn V Second Stage (S-II)
McDonnell Douglas Astronautics Co., Huntington Beach, Calif.	Development and Production of Saturn V Third Stage (S-IVB)

Contractor	**Item**
International Business Machines Federal Systems Div. Huntsville, Ala.	Instrument Unit (Prime Contractor)
Bendix Corp. Navigation and Control Div. Teterboro, N.J.	Guidance Components for Instrument Unit (Including ST-124M Stabilized Platform)
Trans World Airlines, Inc.	Installation Support, KSC
Federal Electric Corp.	Communications and Instrumentation Support, KSC
Bendix Field Engineering Corp.	Launch Operations/Complex Support, KSC
Catalytic-Dow	Facilities Engineering and Modifications, KSC
ILC Industries Dover, Del.	Space Suits
Radio Corp. of America Van Nuys, Calif.	110A Computer — Saturn Checkout
Sanders Associates Nashua, N.H.	Operational Display Systems Saturn
Brown Engineering Hunstville, Ala.	Discrete Controls
Ingalls Iron Works Birmingham, Ala.	Mobile Launchers (structural work)
Smith/Ernst (Joint Venture) Tampa, Fla., Washington, D.C.	Electrical Mechanical Portion of MLs
Power Shovel, Inc. Marion, Ohio	Crawler-Transporter
Hayes International Birmingham, Ala.	Mobile Launcher Service Arms

HOW TO TALK SPACE

blating Materials — Special heat-dissipating materials on the surface of a spacecraft that an be sacrificed (carried away, vaporized) during reentry.

bort — The unscheduled intentional termination of a mission prior to its completion.

ccelerometer — An instrument to sense accelerative forces and convert them into corresponding electrical quantities usually for controlling, measuring, indicating or recording urposes.

dapter Skirt — A flange or extension of a stage or section that provides a ready means f fitting another stage or section to it.

pogee — The point at which a Moon or artificial satellite in its orbit is farthest from Earth.

ttitude — The position of an aerospace vehicle determined by the inclination of its axes to me frame of reference; for Apollo, an inertial, ace-fixed reference is used.

urnout — The point when combustion ceases a rocket engine.

anard — A short, stubby wing-like element affixed to the launch escape tower to provide CM unt end forward aerodynamic capture during abort.

elestial Guidance — The guidance of a vehicle reference to celestial bodies.

elestial Mechanics — The science that deals imarily with the effect of force as an agent determining the orbital paths of celestial dies.

osed Loop — Automatic control units linked gether with a process to form an endless ain.

boost — A retrograde maneuver which lowers ther perigee or apogee of an orbiting spacecraft. Not to be confused with deorbit.

lta V — Velocity change.

gital Computer — A computer in which quanties are represented numerically and which n be used to solve complex problems.

wn-Link — The part of a communication system that receives, processes and displays data om a spacecraft.

hemeris — Orbital measurements (apogee, rigree, inclination, period, etc.) of one celesl body in relation to another at given times. spaceflight, the orbital measurements of a acecraft relative to the celestial body about ich it orbited.

plosive Bolts — Bolts destroyed or severed a surrounding explosive charge which can activated by an electrical impulse.

iring — A piece, part or structure having a ooth, streamlined outline, used to cover a nstreamlined object or to smooth a junction.

ght Control System — A system that serves maintain attitude stability and control during ght.

el Cell — An electromechanical generator in ich the chemical energy from the reaction oxygen and fuel is converted directly into ctricity.

or G Force — Force exerted upon an object gravity or by reaction to acceleration or deration, as in a change of direction: one G the measure of the gravitational pull required accelerate a body at the rate of about 32.16 t-per-second.

nballed Motor — A rocket motor mounted on nbal; i.e., on a contrivance having two mutuy perpendicular axes of rotation, so as to tain pitching and yawing correction moments.

idance System — A system which measures evaluates flight information, correlates this h the target data, converts the result into the conditions necessary to achieve the desired flight path, and communicates this data in the form of commands to the flight control system.

Inertial Guidance — Guidance by means of the measurement and integration of acceleration from onboard the spacecraft. A sophisticated automatic navigation system using gyroscopic devices, accelerometers etc., for high-speed vehicles. It absorbs and interprets such data as speed, position, etc., and automatically adjusts the vehicle to a predetermined flight path. Essentially, it knows where it's going and where it is by knowing where it came from and how it got there. It does not give out any radio frequency signals so it cannot be detected by radar or jammed.

Injection — The process of boosting a spacecraft into calculated trajectory.

Insertion — the process of boosting a spacecraft into an orbit around the Earth or other celestial bodies.

Multiplexing — The simultaneous transmission of two or more signals within a single channel. The three basic methods of multiplexing involve the separation of signals by time division, frequency division and phase division.

Optical Navigation — Navigation by sight, as opposed to inertial methods, using stars or other visible objects as reference.

Oxidizer — In a rocket propellant, a substance such as liquid oxygen or nitrogen tetroxide which supports combustion of the fuel.

Penumbra — Semi-dark portion of a shadow in which light is partly cut off, e.g., surface of Moon or Earth away from Sun. (See umbra.)

Perigee — Point at which a Moon or an artificial satellite in its orbit is closest to the Earth.

Pitch — The angular displacement of a space vehicle about its lateral axis (Y).

Reentry — The return of a spacecraft that reenters the atmosphere after flight above it.

Retrorocket — A rocket that gives thrust in a direction opposite to the direction of the object's motion.

Roll — The angular displacement of a space vehicle about its longitudinal (X) axis.

S-Band — A radio-frequency band of 1,550 to 5,200 megahertz.

Sidereal — Adjective relating to measurement of time, position or angle in relation to the celestial sphere and the vernal equinox.

State vector — Ground-generated spacecraft position, velocity and timing information uplinked to the spacecraft computer for crew use as a navigational reference.

Telemetering — A system for taking measurements within an aerospace vehicle in flight and transmitting them by radio to a ground station.

Terminator — Separation line between lighted and dark portions of celestial body which is not self luminous.

Ullage — The volume in a closed tank or container that is not occupied by the stored liquid; the ratio of this volume to the total volume of the tank; also an acceleration to force propellants into the engine pump intake lines before ignition.

Umbra — Darkest part of a shadow in which light is completely absent, e.g., surface of Moon or Earth away from Sun.

Update pad — Information on spacecraft attitudes, thrust values, event times, navigational data, etc., voiced up to the crew in standard formats according to the purpose, e.g., maneuver update, navigation check, landmark tracking, entry update, etc.

Up-Link Data — Information fed by radio signal from the ground to a spacecraft.

Yaw — Angular displacement of a space vehicle about its vertical (Z) axis.

SPACE ORGANIZATIONS

Adler Planetarium and Astronomical Museum
900 E. Achsah Bond Dr.
Chicago, Illinois 60605

Aerospace Industries Association
1725 DeSales St., N.W.
Washington, D.C. 20036

Air Transport Association of America
1000 Connecticut Ave., N.W.
Washington, D.C. 20036

American Association for the Advancement of Science
1515 Massachusetts Ave., N.W.
Washington, D.C. 20005

American Astronautical Society
P.O. Box 746
Tarzana, Calif. 91356

Also available from John W. Caler
7506 Clybourn
Sun Valley, California 91352

American Astronomical Society
211 Fitz Randolph Rd.
Princeton, N.J. 08540

American Institute of Aeronautics and Astronautics
1290 Sixth Ave.
New York, N.Y. 10019

American Meteorological Society
45 Beacon Street
Boston, Massachusetts 02108

American Museum-Hayden Planetarium
Department of Education
81st Street and Central Park West
New York, New York 10024

American Society for Engineering Education
1346 Connecticut Avenue, N.W.
Washington, D.C. 20036

Civil Air Patrol
National Headquarters
c/o Bookstore,
Maxwell Air Force Base, Alabama 36112

Clearing House for Federal Scientific and Technological Information
Springfield, Virginia 22151

Distribution and Central Film Depository Services-FAD-2
National Aeronautics and Space Administration
Washington, D.C. 20546

Exhibits Division
National Aeronautics and Space Administration
Code FAE
Washington, D.C. 20546

Griffith Observatory and Planetarium
P.O. Box 27787
Griffith Park, Los Angeles, California 90027

Maryland Academy of Sciences
7 West Mulberry Street
Baltimore, Maryland 21201

Mathematical Association of America
SUNY at Buffalo
Buffalo, New York 14214

Morehead Planetarium
University of North Carolina
Chapel Hill, North Carolina 27515

National Academy of Sciences
2101 Constitution Avenue, N.W.
Washington, D.C. 20418

National Aerospace Education Council
Room 616, 806 15th Street, N.W.
Washington, D.C. 20005

National Archives
General Services Administration
Washington, D.C. 20504

National Association of Rocketry
1239 Vermont Avenue, NW
Washington, D.C. 20005

National Council of Technical Schools
1507 M Street, N.W.
Washington, D.C. 20005

National Safety Council
425 North Michigan Avenue
Chicago, Illinois 60611

National Science Foundation
1800 G Street, N.W.
Washington, D.C. 20550

National Society of Professional Engineers
2029 K Street, N.W.
Washington, D.C. 20006

New York Academy of Sciences
2 East 63rd Street
New York, New York 10021

Smithsonian Astrophysical Observatory
60 Garden Street
Cambridge, Massachusetts 02138

Smithsonian Institution
Publications Distribution Section
Washington, D.C. 20560

Superintendent of Documents
U.S. Government Printing Office
Division of Public Documents
Washington, D.C. 20402

U.S. Coast and Geodetic Survey
Public Information Staff
Washington Science Center
Rockville, Maryland 20852